*The Physiology of*
# SENSE ORGANS

# UNIVERSITY REVIEWS IN BIOLOGY

General Editor: J. E. TREHERNE

Advisory Editors: Sir VINCENT WIGGLESWORTH, F.R.S.

M. J. WELLS     T. WEIS-FOGH

## ALREADY PUBLISHED

## IN PREPARATION

# The Physiology of
# SENSE ORGANS

## DeFOREST MELLON, Jr.

*Assistant Professor of Biology,*
*University of Virginia,*
*Charlottesville*

## OLIVER & BOYD
### EDINBURGH AND LONDON

*In Memory of*
*David R. Evans*

OLIVER AND BOYD LTD.

Tweeddale Court
Edinburgh 1

39A Welbeck Street
London W.1

First published .. 1968

© 1968, DeForest Mellon, Jr.

05 001622 9 (Hardback)
05 001682 2 (Paperback)

Printed in Great Britain by
T. and A. Constable Ltd., Edinburgh

# Preface

It is probably safe to say that there is no aspect of an animal's behavior which is not influenced to some extent by the activity of sense organs. Although we can no longer accept the view that behavior is a simple compendium of strictly reflex actions (derived from and triggered by the momentary events which are presented to the peripheral nerves), there can be no doubt that even those aspects which arise endogenously within the central nervous system can be influenced in subtle ways by the appropriate sensory inflow. The precision of the mechanisms by which sensory receptors detect stimulus energy is, thus, critical to the effective functioning of an animal within its environment. All organisms extract energy from their environment in order to exist; sense organs are unique in their ability to sample the quality and magnitude of available energy sources, and to communicate this information to the organism as a whole. We are now vaguely aware that the primary step involves a structural change in the cell membrane, but many details of the problems which have fired the imagination of physiologists for many decades remain unexplained. The earliest—perhaps the most primitive —aspects of the sensory process are still the ones about which we have the least knowledge, and revolutionary techniques may have to be developed before they can be elucidated.

During the early years of this century methods were perfected which, for the first time, made it possible to monitor the electrical activity of peripheral nerves. This entirely new approach to sensory physiology was soon firmly established as attention was focused by Adrian and his colleagues on the intriguing questions raised by the results of psychophysical studies which had been performed during the nineteenth century. An early optimism concerning the ultimate success of this approach was apparently justified; there can be no doubt that the most dramatic advances in the field during the last forty years have been made in the understanding of the electrical events involved in stimulus detection, although this trend has perhaps led to the neglect of other experimental approaches. The six chapters of this book will examine the results of these electrical studies in the light of what is known of the structure and physical properties of the cell membrane. This is admittedly a rather limited aspect of the research presently under way on the perception of environmental stimuli. Sensory cells rarely occur as isolated single elements; usually they are found in large populations —grouped or spatially separate—and they differ variously in terms of their sensitivities to the different parameters of a stimulus. There are thus a host of interesting facets of receptor cell organization and interaction which are outside the scope of this book, as well as the immense problems concerning the mechanisms used by the brain in processing sensory information. How does the brain predict events which are discontinuous in space and time; to take an example, how does a predator track the course of a prey which has momentarily disappeared from sight behind an intervening obstruction? Certainly such a complex procedure involves not only elements of a memory of the preceding sensory events, but also the ability to extend the sequence of these events into the future, and to act on the assumption that such an extension will reflect the actual state of affairs at a forthcoming moment in time. Exciting work is now being done on the cortical arrangements involved with visual perception in mammals, and these findings may well turn out to be the very least that is necessary before we can turn to the type of question presented above. But it all starts with the absorption of stimulus energy by the peripheral nervous system, and the limits of what we perceive are set by the accuracy of our sensory systems. Just how the various sense organs cope with different energy forms presents some unique and baffling problems. Moreover, the electrical events leading to and including impulse initiation are the same for all neurons, and in this respect the findings obtained from more conveniently accessible sensory structures are entirely applicable to cells buried in the central ganglia.

Some excellent collected accounts of symposia on sensory mechanisms have appeared in recent years, and these are recommended to the reader who finds the present book unsatisfactorily general, or specifically unclear. They include: *Sensory Communication*, ed. W. Rosenblith, 1961. M.I.T. Press, Cambridge, Mass.; ' Biological Receptor Mechanisms,' 1962. *Symp. Soc. Exp. Biol.*, 16; ' Sensory Receptors,' *Cold Spring Harbor Symp. quant. Biol.*, 1965. 30.

DeF. M., Jr.

Zoological Laboratory,
Cambridge.
January, 1967

# Contents

# 1: Principles of Stimulus Coding

The detection of environmental stimuli by sensory systems may be conveniently regarded as three sequentially arranged processes; (1) the absorption of stimulus energy, (2) the utilization of absorbed energy to effect microstructural changes in specific regions of the membrane of the sensory cell, and (3) the initiation of nerve impulses. Physiological studies of various sensory receptors have now made it clear that these events may occur either in single cells (primary sensory neurons) or in special two-cell liaisons, as is the case with some visual systems in invertebrates and arthropods and in cells of the vertebrate acoustico-lateralis system. In the latter instances, cells modified for the absorption of external stimulus energy may be incapable of supporting propagated action potentials and respond electrically only by relatively slow potential changes which can be continuously graded in amplitude. These types of cells (hereafter referred to as sensory cells) make functional contact at the periphery with second-order neurons, and conducted impulses which are generated in the latter pass on to the central nervous system. Both types of system have been intensively investigated during recent years, and these studies have served to emphasize many of the common features of receptor mechanisms. Thus, functional distinctions based solely on the point of origin of conducted impulses may not be especially instructive.

Whether a sensory system is modified to detect external energy sources, or changes in the internal environment, the magnitude and rate of change of a stimulus is communicated to the central nervous system by the frequency and number of impulses elaborated at the periphery in primary or second-order

1

nerve cells.  Information about a stimulus is thus pulse-coded, and the correct response which an animal makes to an environmental change depends upon the ability of the central nervous system to interpret correctly the changes in interval between, and/or the number of, impulses which arrive through the individual axonal pathways from each receptor system.  These impulses, or action potentials, are self-propagating potential changes of fixed amplitude.  Among animal groups, they have been evolved and maintained as an apparently universal mechanism for rapidly and precisely conveying information over substantial interorganic distances (fig. 1).

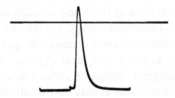

FIG. 1.  An action potential evoked in a crayfish primary sensory neuron by stimulating its axon with a brief electrical shock.  The resting potential of the cell, indicated by the distance between the horizontal straight line and the electrical trace, was about 80 millivolts in magnitude.  The action potential overshoots the zero potential level by about 20 millivolts at its peak amplitude and then decays, as is typical with many crustacean neurons, without any noticeable undershoot of the resting potential level.  The duration of the wave-form at the half-amplitude level is 0·8 milliseconds.

Like many other cell types, neurons and sensory cells maintain a potential difference across their plasma membrane.  Nerve axons are roughly circular in cross-section, and they are hundreds or thousands of times longer than they are wide.  Changes in potential at one site along a nerve are accompanied by current flow across the membrane at that point.  If the ratio of the electrical resistance of the membrane at all points on the axon to that of the internal cytoplasm (axoplasm) were infinitely large, the currents originating at the source would spread for large distances within the axis cylinder, and the potential changes engendered by their movements across the electrical resistance of distant membrane parts could be easily detected. In fact, the ratio of trans-membrane/axoplasmic resistance decreases exponentially with increasing distance along an axon from a source of potential, and the preferential pathway for current is thus across the near membrane, contributing to the progressive decline of longitudinal current flow from the source point (fig. 2). Indeed, with the exception of the largest fibers found in invertebrate preparations (up to 1 mm. in diameter) the complete depolarization of an axon at one region would be undetectable by conventional amplification techniques only one centimeter away. Since many axons are longer than one centimeter—up to a meter or more in vertebrate preparations—variations in the resting potential of the neuronal membrane cannot by themselves be used for analog replication of stimulus intensity, and alternative mechanisms of information transfer have necessarily evolved. A series of proportional voltage amplifiers might foreseeably have been developed by organisms as an alternative to propagated all-or-none type of transmission. As RUSHTON[91] has pointed out, however, the number of separate amplification points logically required in, for example, the length of the nervous pathway involved in the transmission of information from one's finger to the spinal cord, would tend to introduce serious distortions of the amplitude of the original signal unless the accuracy of each stage were unrealistically large. It is the structural uniformity required of such a system that is so difficult to visualize in practical terms. The spread of potential along an axon, for example, depends to a great extent on fiber diameter. Any variation in this parameter would necessarily have to be precisely matched by compensatory alterations in the characteristics of the segmental amplifiers if distortion-free signals were to be transmitted. Now, although pulse-coded systems are theoretically as prone to distortion as any other, in practice time-dependent responding systems can be utilized with a great deal of precision. If the nerve impulse and its recovery processes were determined by the rate constants of one or more self-limiting reactions within the membrane, identical electrical transients would appear at each membrane region during the passage of an action potential down a nerve; only during very high frequencies might the amplitude and time course of an impulse undergo distortion or change, possibly due to a too-rapid utilization of components involved in

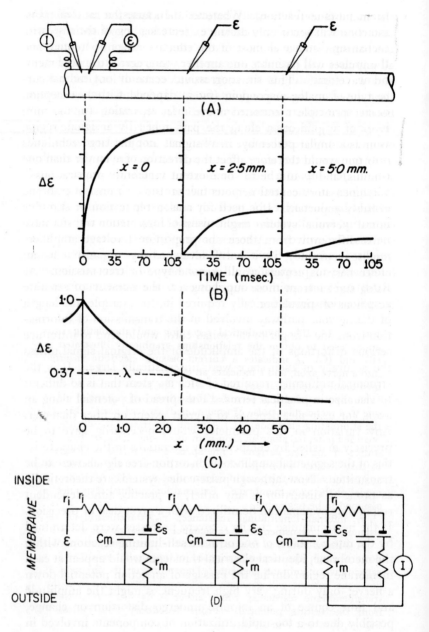

(A)

(B)

(C)

INSIDE

(D)

OUTSIDE

4

the membrane reaction.  Whatever the causes, it is clear that distortion will occur only during extreme loading of the response mechanisms, and over most of the effective range of frequencies all impulses will resemble one another with regard to spike height and waveform.  This situation would certainly not be true of the type of analog-responding system dependent upon a voltage booster principle mentioned above.  In an analog system, any errors of amplification along the path taken by a signal would occur as a similar percentage in all signals, not just large ones, and distortion would therefore affect the detection of even the smallest stimulus, and would be to some extent inherently unpredictable to compensatory central nervous mechanisms.  This last point is probably important.  It is perfectly reasonable to assume that the central nervous system might weight high-frequency impulse trains differently from those showing more moderate rates of impulse recurrence, but it is difficult to envisage any way that the higher nervous centers would know how to detect error-laden analog signals from those supplying a true representation of the conditions of stimulation.

◁ FIG. 2.  (A) The hypothetical recording and stimulating situations used to obtain the relationships graphically illustrated in (B) and (C).  $I$ indicates a current-passing electrode inserted into a nerve axon, and $\varepsilon$ indicates an electrode to record the transmembrane potential at any point.  (B) The time-course and final value of potential change recorded at the three loci illustrated in (A) due to a rectangular pulse of (maintained) current passed through the stimulating electrode.  (C) A graph illustrating the decline in recorded potential along an axon with increasing distance from the source of injected current.  The space constant, $\lambda$, is assigned to that distance within which the recorded potential declines to $37\%$ of its value at the point of current injection.  (D) An electrical model of the axon membrane.  External longitudinal resistance is assumed to be negligible.

$r_l$, internal longitudinal resistance; $r_m$, transmembrane resistance; $C_m$, transmembrane capacitance; $\varepsilon_s$, resting e.m.f.

A current which is injected across the membrane, as in (A), flows through the circuit composed of in-parallel resistive and capacitative membrane elements.  Depending on its direction of flow, the current will generate a potential difference across the transmembrane resistance, which either sums with or subtracts from the resting potential.  (From Woodbury and Patton,[106] Fig. 3$b$, $c$, $d$, and Fig. 18$b$.)

The form and duration of the individual pulses in the frequency code have relatively little bearing upon the way the code is read by the central nervous system. What is important is the number of pulsed events and their frequency of occurrence, and it is this information that must be transmitted in an undistorted fashion. In all metazoan animals the currency unit of the code is the propagated action potential, also called the *nervous impulse.* This is the electrical trace of a brief series of events—actually changes in the permeability characteristics of the nerve cell membrane—which can be triggered in many regions of the cell by an appropriate electrical stimulus, and which, once triggered, can regenerate itself in adjacent membrane areas; thus, it can be propagated to all parts of a cell. The membrane changes occur in sequence, beginning with an increase in the permeability to sodium ions (sodium activation) which rises to a peak value within half a millisecond and is then shut off (sodium inactivation). Shortly after the start of sodium activation a slowly-increasing specific enhancement occurs in the membrane permeability to potassium ions. As will be described below, both types of permeability change are intimately involved in the production of the potential changes associated with the nerve impulse. Here it should be emphasized, however, that the potential changes are not merely by-products of the alterations in membrane permeability; the form and duration of the action potential is strongly influenced by these electrical gradients, without which the permeability changes could neither be triggered nor concluded.[53]

For both sodium and potassium ions there are concentration gradients across the membrane of nerve cells, potassium being more concentrated within the cell and sodium more concentrated in the extracellular fluid. These gradients are maintained both metabolically—by the selective active transport of sodium ions outward across the cell membrane, and potassium ions inward—and also by a Donnan type of electrochemical equilibrium. The latter exists by virtue of the particular permeability properties of the membrane which resists the outward diffusion of large organic anions entrapped within the cytoplasm. The electrostatic attraction of these indiffusible negative groups thus contributes to the maintainance of the high intracellular potassium level. At rest, the nerve membrane is a good deal more permeable to potassium than to sodium, and when this permeability differential is considered with the metabolically maintained separation of sodium and potassium ions on different sides of the membrane, the result is a concentration of potassium forty times greater inside the membrane than in the external solution, and an internal sodium concentration only one-tenth that of its external concentration. Now, since the membrane has at all times a finite permeability to potassium ions, this species tends to diffuse outward across the cell membrane. The associated large organic anions are unable to follow, and the result is an electrostatic charge which makes the inside of the membrane negative to the external environment of the cell. This potential gradient constitutes the so-called *resting potential* of the cell membrane; its magnitude can be theoretically calculated from the following equation of Nernst:

$$E = RT/F \ln(K_o/K_i)$$

where $E$ is the potential difference in millivolts, $T$ the absolute temperature, $R$ the gas constant, $F$ the Faraday constant, and $K_o$ and $K_i$ are the concentration of potassium ions on the outside and the inside of the membrane respectively. In most nerve cells this relationship only approximates the electrical and ionic concentration conditions which exist across the membrane. The reasons for this departure from predicted theory are several and not entirely understood. One fairly obvious possibility is that the discrepancy results from the finite permeability of the membrane to sodium ions, so that this ion species continuously diffuses inward. The resulting potential would thus tend to reduce substantially that created by the outward diffusion of potassium. In addition, the permeability characteristics of the membrane are not constant and, as will be discussed below, are rather dependent upon the voltage gradient across the neuronal membrane. None the less, most nerve cells in the resting state exhibit a steady potential difference of about 75 millivolts across the membrane, the inside being negative to the outside.

It will now be useful to examine in greater detail the sequential permeability changes which occur during the action potential. As mentioned above, the earliest event in the sequence is a marked increase in membrane permeability toward sodium ions. Now, an electrical, as well as a concentration, gradient occurs across the membrane, and both tend to drive sodium into the cell. The increased permeability to this ion thus results in an immediate inward current, depolarizing the membrane in surrounding regions. In fact, during the brief time that sodium ions are actually flowing into the cell, the membrane potential actually reverses to a value of about 45 millivolts more positive on the inside than on the outside. This potential difference is close to the electrochemical equilibrium potential of sodium ions in the system, and presumably it would be maintained as long as the selective permeability to sodium were to continue. However, the depolarization itself triggers a membrane reaction which, after a brief period, reverses the sodium activation and inactivates the mechanism responsible for the increased permeability to this ion species. At the same time, there is a slow increase in the permeability of the membrane to potassium ions. It is, in fact, the facilitated outward movement of these ions that constitutes the falling phase of the nerve impulse. The driving force which accounts for their outward movement is of course the highly positive state on the inside of the cell during the action potential; the increased membrane permeability merely increases the already finite mobility of potassium through the membrane structure, and this movement restores the membrane potential toward its resting value. The electrochemical equilibrium potential for potassium ions in the system is roughly 90 millivolts, the inside being negative to the bathing medium. This explains the tendency, seen with many nerve cells, for the falling phase of the action potential to undershoot the resting level of membrane potential; the increased permeability of the membrane to potassium during the falling phase means that the cell's membrane potential is dominated by this ionic current to a greater extent than it would be otherwise. However, the hyperpolarizing undershoot at the end of the action potential inactivates the enhanced potassium permeability, so that the membrane potential once again returns to resting values.

The rather complex series of events described above offers no explanation for the propagated nature of the action potential, i.e. its unique ability to re-establish itself in immediately adjacent membrane regions and thus spread throughout the cell. A clue to the operation of this mode of propagation is in the very nature of the only effective trigger for an action potential—membrane depolarization. The only known way to initiate a nervous impulse is to pass an outward current across an inactive region of cell membrane and thereby depolarize it below its threshold for excitation. As soon as this occurs, sodium activation is triggered, and the explosive increase in membrane permeability to this ion is the result. Now, the dense inward current which occurs during the rising phase of the action potential spreads longitudinally within the axon from the active region and recrosses the membrane (probably as an outward flow of potassium ions) in adjacent areas. Momentarily, the resting capacitative charge on the membrane is reduced by this outward current, and this depolarization triggers the increase in sodium conductance in the new region of membrane. Thus, the currents which are generated by the impulse itself are responsible for its renewed appearance farther along the nerve. Now, action currents probably spread in both directions along the axon from their immediate point of entry. In the region of the nerve through which the action potential has just passed, however, a refractory state of the membrane is encountered—perhaps due to persistent sodium inactivation—and the currents fail to trigger another impulse at that locus. By the time the membrane has recovered sufficiently to support another impulse, the first is a considerable distance away, and the fraction of its current crossing the earlier locus of activity is small indeed.

Action potentials, therefore, appear to constitute just the type of coupled, time-dependent mechanisms which would be free from distortion, except at relatively high frequencies. The energy for such mechanisms derives from the existence of the metabolically maintained ionic and potential gradients across the neuronal membrane. The time constants of the membrane events controlling the permeability to sodium and potassium ions determine the amplitude and temporal characteristics of the action potential; it is the number and frequency of these transients which constitute the meaningful code of the transmitted signal.

An investigation of the quantitative relationships between the magnitude of the applied stimulus and the frequency of the consequent nervous discharge could not be examined rigorously until means were found for recording the electrical activity of

S.O.—B

only one sensory neuron at a time. This was first successfully accomplished in 1926 by ADRIAN and ZOTTERMAN[4] using the *sterno-cutaneous* muscle of the frog. This muscle, which contains only three or four stretch-sensitive sensory nerve cells, was systematically dissected until the afferent fiber from only a single end-organ remained intact and active. The results of these studies demonstrated conclusively, in records uncomplicated by multifiber discharges, that primary sensory neurons respond to an increase in the intensity of an adequate stimulus by augmenting the frequency of propagated impulses.

More precise measurements of the relationships between stimulus intensity and impulse frequency were made several years later by MATTHEWS[76] in a systematic series of investigations using a more routinely accessible preparation. MATTHEWS was the first to observe the well-known logarithmic relationship between stimulus strength and steady impulse frequency, to which many sensory cells have been subsequently shown to approximate.

Now, there are theoretical and practical limits to the maximum frequency capabilities of the neuronal membrane. The finite duration of the action potential and its recovery processes fix this limit at about 1000 per second, although even higher values than this can occur in a few cases among vertebrates. At the same time, the threshold of a receptor must be sufficiently low so that small but significant amounts of stimulus energy—or changes in available energy—can be detected by the organism. While, theoretically, there is really no lower limit to the frequency response of a neuron (unless it be less than once in the life span!), in practice, the survival of most metazoans depends upon a nervous system having individual units which operate with time-constants of the order of milliseconds. A sensory response of one impulse per 100 seconds would normally be quite useless in terms of information content, since it would be indistinguishable from background noise to cells in the central nervous system. In practical terms, a lower limit of one impulse per second can be chosen as a meaningful threshold frequency. Now, many external sense organs are routinely presented with stimulus energies extending over an enormous range—at least $10^{10}$ in photosensitive cells. Even if the maximum frequency response of a sensory neuron approached 1000 per second, even relatively large changes in stimulus energy would, in a linear transforming system, be signalled only by very small changes in frequency of impulses.  A hypothetical photosensory neuron which was sensitive to light energies over the entire available range ($10^{10}$) would, in response to an increase of light intensity by a factor of $10^7$, increase its firing frequency by only one impulse per second.  Such small frequency increments would possibly augment, in a statistical manner, the detectable input from large numbers of individual sensory cells;  however, it is extremely unlikely that changes of this magnitude could be correctly interpreted by the higher nervous centers on a single neuronal basis;  for random fluctuations in events at central synapses probably exceed in amplitude any individual response increment of one part in $10^7$.

One obvious way to circumvent the apparent incompatibility of high sensitivity to stimulus energies and the broad dynamic range of the nerve cells involved would be the provision of several different populations of primary neurons or sensory cells.  In such an arrangement each population would respond to the same stimulus modality or quality, but collectively they would have dynamic ranges which would overlap and would vary in sensitivity over several orders of magnitude.  In fact, there is adequate evidence that such a principle of functional division among sensory cells does operate in many animals.  The acoustic organs of Noctuid moths provide an exceptionally striking example.  Sensory neurons in these organs are capable of responding to sounds over a broad frequency spectrum in the ultrasonic range.  These cells are, in fact, able to detect the sounds emitted by predacious bats, and their signals influence the behavior of the moth when stimuli of this nature are encountered.  It is, perhaps, surprising that the detection of such compressional energy appears to be accomplished by only two pairs of primary sensory neurons—one pair innervating the acoustic organ on either side of the animal.  Although both auditory cells of a pair respond to the same broad frequency range of sound, one cell on each side is more sensitive (by about 20 decibels) than its partner.[88]  Thus, as the intensity of an artificially generated ultrasonic pulse is increased—or as a hunting bat approaches the moth—the frequency and number of impulses in the more sensitive neurons increase, to be augmented later by discharge of action potentials in the cells with the higher threshold (fig. 3).

An alternative method of monitoring broad ranges in stimulus energy is to transform the energy in terms of a logarithmic function, a principle which was first observed in single sensory elements thirty-five years ago.[76] At high stimulus intensities, the increase in energy required to bring about a given increase in impulse frequency may be several orders of magnitude greater than it is at threshold. Many sensory neurons display this type of behavior (fig. 4, A–C), which is now regarded as a general condition. The mechanisms responsible for a logarithmic transformation are far from clear, however. SHERRINGTON[94] once stated that sensory end-organs are structures for lowering the threshold of the nerve to a specific form of energy; although the simplicity of this view might now be embellished with the results of many sophisticated electrical investigations which have been performed since its enunciation sixty years ago, we are very little closer to understanding the initial mechanisms involved in the energy absorption process. The difficulty in our way is mainly our present inability to define the energy-utilizing reactions of the membrane to a given stimulus; in other words, we are ignorant of the precise changes which happen to the membrane's molecular architecture when energy is absorbed. Nor is it clear precisely which form of energy is most effective in producing these changes. In studies on mechanoreceptors, for example, stimulation is variously measured in terms of muscle tension, shearing forces applied to a cuticular sensillum, or compression of the receptor structure. One critical question is what exact percentage of the applied energy is actually used in the alteration of membrane structure leading to impulse initiation. An example will illustrate current confusion in this aspect of sensory physiology. In the crustacean muscle stretch-receptor organs, the adequate stimulus is probably the deformation of the sensory nerve-endings which are imbedded in the receptor muscle, and this can be brought about either by increases in muscle length or tension. However, the impulse frequency in the sensory neuron is a linear function of muscle length, but a logarithmic function of muscle tension. It has been pointed out that muscle does not obey HOOKE'S Law[37]; thus, the data obtained may be explained by the possibility that the

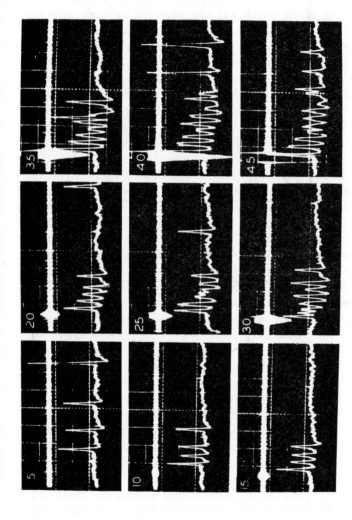

FIG. 3. Electrical recordings from the cells in one tympanic organ of a moth in response to pulses of high frequency sound. As the intensity of the sound is increased (from 5 to 45), action potentials are generated by first one, then a second sensory neuron, and the frequency and number of impulses from each cell increases. Relative sound energy is indicated by the height of the envelope, shown on the upper trace in each frame. The two large spikes in the frame numbered 40 are from a non-auditory neuron. (From Roeder and Treat.[88])

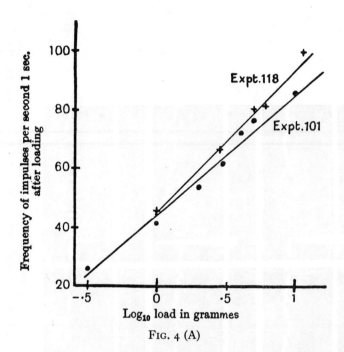

FIG. 4 (A)

FIG. 4 (B)

14

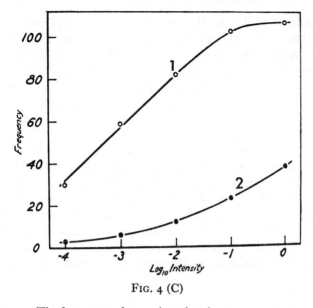

FIG. 4 (C)

FIG. 4. The frequency of nerve impulses in sensory neurons as a function of the intensity of the stimulus. (A) Response of a primary stretch-sensitive neuron in the frog toe to loading.[76] (B) Impulse frequency in a primary salt receptor neuron of a blowfly when challenged with various concentrations of aqueous sodium chloride.[34] (C) the response of a second-order sensory neuron, the eccentric cell, in the compound eye of *Limulus* to white light of different intensities : (1) steady-response phase, (2) initial phase of response. (A from Matthews,[76] Fig. 7; B from Gillary,[34] Fig. 3; C from Hartline and Graham,[48] Fig 6.)

adequate stimulus (tension) increases logarithmically with increments in length, and therefore the linear increase in impulse frequency with length may represent the usual logarithmic stimulus-response relationship. In any case, it is clear that the mere presence of a logarithmic stimulus transformation in different sense organs should not be taken to indicate a common mechanism of stimulus transduction.

In addition to the difficulties involved in arriving at an adequate definition of stimulus utilization energy, there are also uncertainties in the measurement of response magnitude. Now the output of most receptors is a function not only of absolute stimulus

15

strength, but also of the period since the application of the stimulus. Sensory neurons whose output frequency declines most rapidly with time, or which respond only during actual changes in stimulus strength, are arbitrarily classified as *phasic*. *Tonic* sensory cells, on the other hand, are those which reproduce the time-course of stimulus application more faithfully (even if, in some cases, this involves a steady-frequency output for hours). As a general rule, however, all neurons fire with higher impulse frequencies immediately following stimulus onset. The subsequent decline in frequency is usually taken as the neural correlate of sensory adaptation (a phenomenon which has been recognized for a hundred years) and almost certainly results from at least two independent processes (Chapter 3). Some sense organs (usually classed as tonic) have, in fact, two distinct phases of activity—an initial burst of impulses, followed by a phase which declines at a much slower rate (fig. 5). However, the two phases may not show

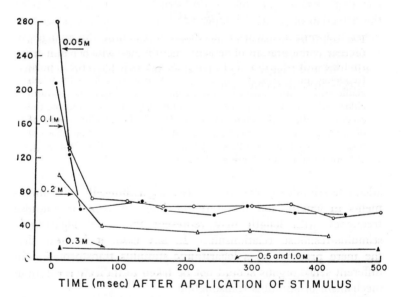

TIME (m sec) AFTER APPLICATION OF STIMULUS

FIG. 5. Impulse frequency as a function of time in a primary water-sensitive neuron of the blowfly, *Phormia*. Both the initial high-frequency phase and the steady phase of the response are reduced by the addition of small amounts of sodium chloride (0.05−0.3 M), but to different extents. (From Evans and Mellon,[25] Fig. 6.)

similar relationships to the strength of the applied stimulus, and it should therefore be evident that quantitative comparisons between different receptors, or the different responses of a single cell to different stimulus intensities, should include a statement of the period during which the measurements were made.

Disparities in the time-course of the sensory response, as described above, contribute to the difficulties involved in arriving at a quantitative analysis of the effects of stimulus magnitude, and, therefore, in investigating excitatory mechanisms at the molecular level. Some of these difficulties are amenable to an eventual electrophysiological solution, such as deciding what factors are responsible for the phasic and tonic properties of impulse generating regions of neuronal membranes. But at the present time it is often difficult to pose proper questions about the nature of the changes, induced by the stimulus, at the level of the membrane architecture. It is difficult even to give an explanation for the fact that certain types of sensory structure are associated with the detection of particular types of stimuli. Probably other biophysical approaches will be necessary to examine the changes in molecular configuration of sensory membranes which result from a stimulus and trigger the electrical events that have been studied so successfully in recent years.

# 2 : The Depolarizing Nature
## of the Trigger

Changes in electrical potential which are associated with excitation in receptor structures have been known for over a hundred years. HOLMGREN[54] is usually credited with the discovery in 1865 of the electroretinogram—the slow graded change in potential difference across the retinal layer of the eye which results from photic stimulation. Since HOLMGREN's time, amplitude-graded potential changes have been recorded from other sensory systems having a large population of receptor cells, notably the vertebrate ear and organs of the lateral line in fish.[56] In all these cases, where numerous cells contribute to the recorded signal, the synchronous activation by an appropriate stimulus produces sizeable potential gradients across the sensory structures, and they can be detected with relatively unsophisticated techniques.

The recognition that nerve cells, as distinct from non-neural sensory cells, are also able to support graded electrical activity has come about only within the last thirty years. In the early 1930s it seems to have been appreciated by physiologists that some sort of graded sustained electrical change within a neuron might account for the control of impulse frequency and number. The first experimental evidence, however, directly implicating graded neuronal activity was not obtained until 1937. In that year and the next, the results of research efforts in two separate laboratories provided evidence to support the contention that nerve axons are intrinsically capable of generating localized electrically-evoked activity which can be graded in amplitude by varying the intensity of the stimulus. KATZ[57] deduced the presence of such activity as the only logical explanation for observations that localized regions of axons in the vicinity of the stimulating cathode remained hyperexcitable for varying periods following a sub-threshold conditioning shock. Since the period of raised sensitivity was too long to be explained by the residual polarization from the conditioning shock—a phenomenon resulting from the finite time taken to recharge the nerve membrane capacitance—it was concluded that local sub-threshold activity of the fiber was responsible for the period of heightened excitability. Within the same year, HODGKIN[50] was able, by electrical records from single crustacean axons, to provide direct proof of the existence of this type of activity. Many crustacean peripheral nerves are only loosely invested with connective tissue, and, as a result, individual nerve fibers can be rather easily separated from the main bundle. Preparations of this kind are particularly well suited for extracellular recordings of low-amplitude transmembrane events; the axons are unusually large, being 30–50 microns in diameter, and the proportion of active to inactive tissue is consequently greater than that found in multifibered preparations. Now, since inactive tissue not only adds nothing to the electrical potentials generated during membrane activity, but provides for a lower extracellular resistance in the environment of the active tissue, focal activity along a nerve with a good deal of extraneous tissue is subjected to an amount of short-circuiting by non-active conductor; in single-fiber preparations short-circuiting of this sort is considerably reduced, and the signal-to-noise ratio is correspondingly increased.

Figure 6 illustrates some of HODGKIN'S original records. With small shocks, both anodal and cathodal pulses produced identically-shaped potential changes at the neighboring recording electrode. In both cases, the smooth exponential decay of potential due to small current pulses is diagnostic of a recharging membrane capacitance, following the transient alteration of the resting potential by the impressed stimulus. Larger cathodal shocks (which were, however, still sub-threshold for impulse initiation) produced in the membrane close to the point of stimulus application an electrical response which had a time-course undeniably longer than that occasioned by the passive decay of charge. This effect could not be evoked when stimulus polarity was reversed, i.e.

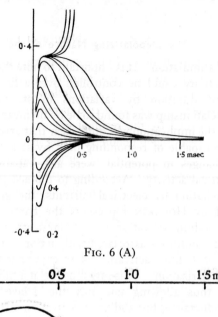

FIG. 6 (A)

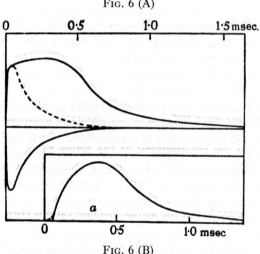

FIG. 6 (B)

FIG. 6.  (A) Oscillograph traces representing the responses of a single crustacean nerve fiber to single, brief cathodal and anodal electric stimuli.  The responses to increasing strengths of cathodal stimulus are shown as upward deflections of the oscillograph trace.  They mirror the responses to corresponding strengths of anodal current when they are of sub-threshold value.  At threshold, cathodal shocks evoke prolonged local membrane responses which can trigger action potentials, three of which are shown (truncated).  (B) Local membrane response (*a*) obtained by subtraction of passive residual potential (dotted line) from the potential record obtained in response to a barely threshold cathodal stimulus.  An anodal stimulus of identical intensity (downward deflection) generates only a passive decay of potential, due to recharging of the membrane capacitance.  (From Hodgkin,[50] Figs. 7 and 8.)

20

during anodal stimulation. It is important to note that the cathod-
ally-evoked activity could be controlled over a limited range of
amplitude and duration by variations in stimulus strength,
although the relationship was found to be by no means a linear one.
Nevertheless, the implication was quite clear that axons, previously
thought to be capable of responding only by strictly all-or-none
propagated changes in potential, were also capable of graded,
localized electrical activity. According to the accepted theory of
membrane excitation by electrical currents, the graded activity
first observed by HODGKIN represents the barely unsuccessful
attempt of the sodium activation mechanism to attain the explosive
self-generating conditions associated with action potentials. The
rate of onset of sodium activation is an exponential function of
membrane depolarization. This rate must be at a minimum in the
present case, thus allowing not only the delayed increase in
potassium conductance, but sodium inactivation also, to interfere
successfully with the activation process. With a barely perceptible
increase in stimulus intensity, the local response will increase at a
progressively greater rate, reaching a higher amplitude before it is
removed by the restorative processes just mentioned. At threshold,
an impulse will be generated at maximum latency by the response,
and as the stimulus strength is increased still further, the rate of
rise of the response also increases, with an attendant decrease in
latency for spike triggering. This is an important point; for, as
will be discussed in a later chapter, local response growth appears
to be an important controlling factor in discharge frequency of
sensory neurons. It should be noted, however, that most naturally-
occurring membrane changes which evoke local responses in sensory neurons are of considerably longer duration than the transient
electrical shocks used in HODGKIN's experiments, and significantly
different strength-latency relationships are to be expected.

The discovery of the axonal local response was a conceptual
breakthrough which extended the theoretical, as well as the
practical, implications of the neuron as a responding unit. However, the major problems with regard to anatomical and physiological modification of the regions of sensory neurons concerned
with analog stimulus replication remained unanswered. Yet, it
was becoming increasingly clear that the generation of conducted
impulses must logically be preceded by a sustained electrical

change across part of the membrane of the neuron. The evidence for this kind of activity was still largely circumstantial, and arguments were taken, for example, from observations on the effect of injury upon nervous activity. Thus, in 1932 ADRIAN[3] had stated, ' Whether or not depolarization explains the discharge from sense organs, there is no doubt that injury, which involves permanent depolarization, can set up a rhythmic discharge in a nerve fiber. These injury discharges are abnormal effects, but the injured and active states are so closely allied that it is worth spending a little time over them. Both give the same potential change, for both involve a breakdown in the polarized surface membrane, though in the intact fiber the breakdown is promptly repaired.' Another argument utilized the fact that repetitive responses can be evoked in axons by prolonged pulses of depolarizing current.[8, 51] It was found that impulse trains thus generated could be rather precisely controlled, both in frequency and duration, by variations in the amplitude and time-course of the stimulus current. Thus, it was argued that if some region of the sense cell membrane were able to generate similar prolonged currents under the influence of a natural stimulus, repetitive firing of the neuron could be presumed to result, the impulse frequency being a direct function of stimulus intensity.[15] Graded long-lasting variations in potential were, in fact, observed by HARTLINE and GRAHAM[48] in their original (and now classic) observations on the Limulus compound eye. What made these findings so remarkable, in the face of several earlier observations[30] on slow potential changes in visual systems, was their appearance in what were then believed to be true primary sensory neurons, rather than non-neural sensory cells. It is now realized that the interpretation of these records was oversimplified; the investigators were undoubtedly recording impulse activity in second-order neurons—the eccentric cells—which are driven to activity by strictly graded electrical changes in the primary sensory, or retinula, cells.[10, 100] There is still some controversy regarding the ability of the latter to support propagated regenerative electrical activity; in either case, the slow potential change in the baseline of the records obtained by HARTLINE and GRAHAM can be interpreted as a summation of the graded response of both the retinula cells and the eccentric cell itself.[49, 107]

An interesting model sense organ was examined in 1946 by BERNHARD and GRANIT,[15] which exhibited electrical characteristics similar to those that had been proposed for primary sensory neurons. The model consisted of a length of cat sciatic nerve which was caused to fire impulses in a repetitive fashion by local cooling of a restricted region near one end. With an electrode pair placed so as to record the steady potential difference between the cooled region of the nerve and another region five centimeters away, it was possible to detect that the former region became electrically negative during the application of the stimulus. This effect was reversible, and it is presumed that the maintained cathodal potential was acting as the generator of the impulse trains. This finding lent support to the theory that sustained electrical changes in sensory neurons are the natural triggers for impulses arising in these structures.

It was not until 1950, however, that the first electrical records were obtained which unequivocally demonstrated the presence of a graded and sustained generator potential within a primary sensory neuron. The credit for this discovery belongs to BERNARD KATZ,[58, 59] who reinvestigated a preparation which had been made famous twenty-five years earlier by ADRIAN, namely, the frog muscle spindle. Now vertebrate muscle receptor organs are supplied by primary sensory neurons whose axons originate from cells within the central nervous system. Characteristically, the fibers are myelinated except for their terminal portions, which are inserted into the end-organ. In some muscles, which control the movement of the toes in the frog, the number of sensory axons per muscle is small, the individual axons being 30 to 60 microns in diameter. KATZ was thus able to account for all the nerve fibers entering the particular muscle he used and, subsequently, to transect all nervous connections, save for a single axon. The inset in figure 7 illustrates the recording arrangement used for the detection of graded electrical activity. If the length of sensory nerve between the spindle end-organ and the active recording lead, $E_2$, was sufficiently short, sustained low-amplitude potential changes, as well as trains of action potentials, were recorded by a direct coupled amplifier as a result of applying stretch to the spindle. Typical records are shown in figure 7. KATZ was especially careful in interpreting the records obtained with these procedures. Two

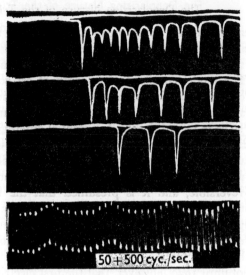

50+500 cyc./sec.

FIG. 7 (A)

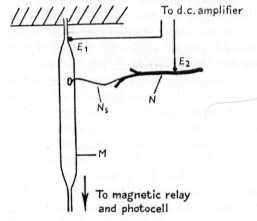

To d.c. amplifier

$E_1$

$E_2$

$N_s$

$N$

$M$

To magnetic relay
and photocell

FIG. 7 (B)

FIG. 7. (A) Extracellular records of electrical activity in a single stretch-sensitive neuron of the frog. Nerve impulses arise from a maintained depolarization, the receptor potential. Larger degrees of stretch evoke receptor potentials of higher amplitude, which, in turn, generate impulse trains of increased frequency.

(B) Diagram of the recording situation. $M$ receptor muscle; $N_s$ single remaining afferent fiber. $E_1$, $E_2$ indifferent and active recording leads, respectively. (From Katz,[59] Fig. 6C.)

24

particularly pertinent alternative possibilities could be suggested concerning the origin of the observed graded changes in potential: (1) since the receptor muscle was included between the active and indifferent electrodes, it could be argued that intrinsic potential changes generated by the muscle fibers themselves accounted for the recorded activity; and (2) the sustained potential variations observed during stretch of the receptor, with the accompanying impulse trains, could represent an electrical summation of residual after-potentials from the individual impulses. Experimental evidence produced by KATZ quite clearly militates against both of these possibilities. Short-circuiting the nerve, by laying it on the muscle itself, consistently abolished stretch-induced potential changes. Crushing the sensory axon at its point of entry into the muscle also had a similar effect. Neither of these procedures would have interfered with electrotonically-recorded activity originating in the muscle tissue itself; but they certainly would be expected to prevent the detection of current flow from a source of potential in the nerve-ending. Two other arguments are relevant to the second objection. Firstly, most observations showed a negative shift in the potential baseline which occurred before the generation of the first action potential, thus eliminating the possibility that it was some form of afterpotential. In the second place, it was shown that the generator potential remained virtually unchanged in both amplitude and duration, after all impulse activity had been suppressed by the addition of procaine to the bathing solution. The remarkable records shown in figure 8 thus allowed direct observations to be made on the relationship between the strength of the stimulus, its time-course, and rate of application to the amplitude and duration of the graded generator potential. In all cases, these observations were from the superimposed electrical interference of an impulse discharge. Some of these findings, in particular the quantitative relationship between stimulus intensity and receptor potential amplitude, will be discussed in Chapter 3. Perhaps a more important observation (utilizing the differential effect of the procaine) was the demonstration of the separate physiological nature of the membrane regions which generated, respectively, the action and the graded receptor potentials.[73] Other major differences between these two types of membrane response may be gathered from the records illustrated in figure 7.  For example, typical all-or-none action potentials occurred, while the receptor potentials were of a graded nature, their amplitude and duration depending upon stimulus parameters.   In addition, the impulses

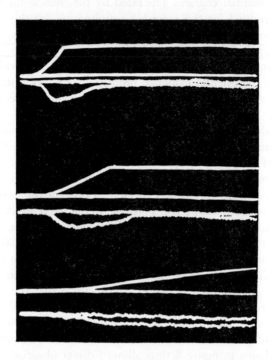

FIG. 8.    Time-course and amplitude of the receptor potential in the frog stretch receptor.   The preparation has been treated with procaine to abolish impulse activity.   Upward deflection monitors the degree and rate of stretch applied to the receptor muscle.   Electrical activity of the nerve ending is recorded by the lower traces.   (From Katz,[59] Fig. 13B.)

were actively propagated along the sensory axon, while the spread of the receptor potential was clearly decremental.   On the other hand, differences between the receptor potential and the local responses of the type described by HODGKIN[50] are less obvious and require careful consideration.   Now, the current interpretation of the process of impulse generation in nerve and muscle assumes that most graded electrical events—receptor and synaptic potentials —arise in regions of membrane whose conductance characteristics are not affected by the passage of electric currents, although they may be profoundly altered by the application of other types of stimulus energy (see, however, the discussion of electroreceptors in Chapter 4). A corollary to this doctrine of 'electrical inexcitability'[40, 41] is that neither synaptic nor receptor types of electrogenesis are actively propagated to adjacent regions of the membrane, and local currents, flowing as a result of an applied stimulus, spread only decrementally along the cell. These currents thus resemble the electrotonic spread of artificially generated anodal, or sub-threshold cathodal, electric shocks, in that there is no active propagation of the electrical disturbance to distant parts of the cell. Potentials of this type may also resemble in their behavior the local response which can be recorded from electrically excitable membrane. And, although HODGKIN showed that such local activity can propagate to varying extents along an axon, these distances are exceedingly short unless a full action potential is triggered. The local response however shares with the action potential the property of refractoriness, i.e. a period of absolute, and then relative, inexcitability following previous activity. Thus, after one local response has decayed to zero, a finite interval must elapse before a second response can be evoked in that region of the nerve membrane. No such restriction applies to the receptor potential of any sensory cell so far examined, whether neural or non-neural. Sub-maximal receptor potentials will summate at all intervals of time, as was first demonstrated with the Pacinian corpuscle—a particularly accessible type of mammalian mechanosensory neuron.[6, 39] The response characteristics of these receptors are dominated by the mechanical properties of the capsule which surrounds the nerve-ending (fig. 23). As a rule, the intact receptor adapts very rapidly, even to prolonged stimuli, and the receptor potentials (occurring in response to mechanical stimulation) decay within a few milliseconds. These brief responses can be continuously graded in amplitude by variations in stimulus intensity, and electrical summation occurs at brief intervals of stimulation, indicating absence of any appreciable period of absolute refractoriness (fig. 9).

By the early 1950s, therefore, several functional distinctions

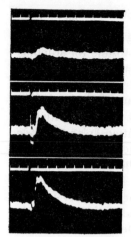

FIG. 9. (A) Graded increases in receptor potential magnitude (lower traces) in response to increases in strength of a mechanical stimulus (monitored on upper traces). (B) Summation of paired responses as the interval between equal-strength mechanical stimuli was reduced. Time marks appear at one millisecond intervals. (From Gray and Sato,[39] Figs. 6 and 13.)

FIG. 9 (A)

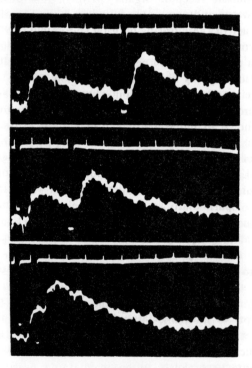

FIG. 9 (B)

could be drawn between the spike generating membrane, on the one hand, and those membrane regions responsible for stimulus transduction, on the other.  Important questions still remained as to the functional relationship between receptor potential magnitude and impulse threshold and frequency.  The definitive answers to these questions could only be revealed with the development of suitable preparations using intracellular electrode techniques, which would enable reliable measurements of the absolute values for receptor potentials to be made at various regions of the sensory neuron.  It was not long before such a preparation was found.  It consisted of the large primary sensory neurons which function as stretch detectors and are a characteristic feature of the neuroanatomy of Macruran Decapod crustaceans. Especially notable are those which are associated with the abdominal muscle receptor organs (MROs), first described by ALEXANDROWICZ[5] and commonly found in lobsters and crayfish. There is a pair of these organs on each abdominal hemisegment, making a complement of four in each segment.  Each organ consists of a primary sensory neuron and a small dorsally-located muscle, which are so arranged that flexion of the abdomen stretches the muscle and, if tension is strong enough, excites the sensory neuron.[66, 102]  A representation of a single pair of these MROs is shown in figure 10, which shows the large dendritic branches which proliferate from each roughly-pyramidal cell body and imbed themselves in the structure of the muscle.  The organs are readily accessible for dissection purposes and remain in functional condition for several hours when isolated in an appro-priate physiological solution.  Moreover, the muscles associated with the sensory neurons can be removed in an intact condition, so that passive and active stimulation of the sensory dendrites can occur very much as happens under natural circumstances.  It is interesting to find that there are physiological differences, not only between the two sensory neurons of a pair, but also (and compar-ably) between the muscle fibers of the two organs.  Thus, one neuron adapts to mechanical stimuli quite rapidly and is most effectively activated by rapid changes in the tension of its associated muscle (which consists of phasic twitch-type fibers); the other neuron adapts very slowly, often maintaining nearly constant firing frequencies for periods of an hour or longer.  The muscle

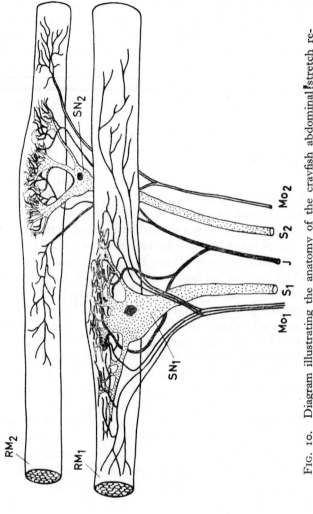

FIG. 10. Diagram illustrating the anatomy of the crayfish abdominal stretch receptors. *SN* sensory neurons supplying receptor muscles 1 and 2 (*RM₁, RM₂*); *Mo* motoneurons to the receptor muscles; *S* axons of the sensory neurons; *J* inhibitory nerve fiber. (From Autrum,[8] Fig. 15.)

associated with the latter neuron is of the tonic type, which develops and loses tension much more gradually than the twitch-type one. Much of the experimental work described below was obtained from the slowly-adapting neuron, since the state of excitation of this cell remains relatively constant and the mechanical threshold for impulse initiation is usually lower than that of the fast-adapting cell. Changes in effective stimulus strength can thus be performed with much smaller manipulations of the preparation. The latter feature confers considerable advantage, because of the critical geometrical relationship which exists between the impaled neuron and the comparatively rigid glass recording micropipette.

The records in figures 11 and 12, which have now become

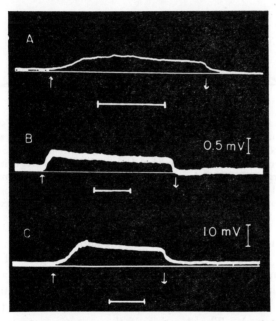

FIG. 11. Intracellular recordings from crustacean abdominal stretch receptor neurons. (A) Slowly-adapting neuron; onset and cessation of stretch indicated by arrows. (C) Rapidly-adapting cell. (B) Extracellular records from a slowly-adapting neuron which had been treated with 0·1 per cent novocaine. Voltage calibration the same for (A) and (C). Horizontal bars all indicate one second. (From Eyzaguirre and Kuffler,[27] Fig. 3.)

classics in the neurophysiological literature, are taken from the work of EYZAGUIRRE and KUFFLER,[27] who were the first to investigate this preparation with microelectrodes. In these experiments the potential changes were detected by means of a recording pipette inserted in the soma. The potential change observed therefore consisted of soma action potentials as well as depolarizing receptor potentials caused by stretch of the MRO and deformation of the dendritic branches in the associated

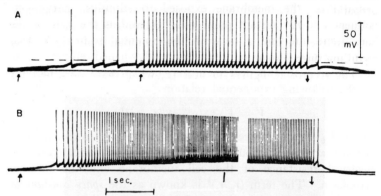

FIG. 12. Intracellular records from a slowly-adapting stretch receptor neuron of the crayfish, showing action potentials superimposed upon stretch-induced receptor potentials. (A) Stretch increased and then maintained at low levels to show regularity of discharge. (B) Stretch gradually increased between first arrow and vertical line, then maintained for several seconds (missing part of record). Note slight hyperpolarization following relaxation. (From Eyzaguirre and Kuffler,[27] Fig. 5.)

sensory neuron. It was found that the amplitude of the receptor potential could be finely controlled by the degree of passive stretch applied to the receptor muscle. This effect appeared uncomplicated by impulse activity until it reached an amplitude of about 10 mV (in slowly-adapting cells) or 20 mV (in fast-adapting ones). The duration of the receptor potential in the slowly-adapting neuron was essentially equivalent to that of the applied stimulus. When an applied stretch was sufficiently intense, nerve impulses appeared in the electrical records (fig. 12). Although the regularity of the discharge tended to be less constant at threshold than at higher amplitudes of depolarization, control over firing frequency by the amplitude of the receptor potential could be achieved with some precision. As the authors so vividly described it, ' . . . the present preparation provides a cell which can be poised delicately on the verge of activity, maintained in activity, accelerated or depressed—all through mechanisms within the dendrites, not necessarily involving axon-type conduction '.[27]

Since the receptor potential spreads decrementally throughout a sensory neuron from the locus of its origin—normally the point(s) on the membrane exposed to stimulus energy,—its influence at any distant point will decrease as the area of the membrane intervening between the potential source and that point increases. In a uniform cylindrically-shaped cell projection, such as an axon, this decrement may be expressed quantitatively by the following exponential relation:

$$V = V_0 \exp \left[ -x/(r_m/r_i)^{\frac{1}{2}} \right]$$

where $V_0$ is the source voltage, $V$ the voltage measured at a distance $x$ from the source, and $r_m$ and $r_i$ are, respectively, the electrical resistance of the cell membrane and the internal cytoplasm. The term $(r_m/r_i)^{\frac{1}{2}}$ is known as the *space constant* of the axon under examination, and it is numerically equal to the distance within which the original voltage $(V_0)$ falls to $1/e$, or about 37 per cent. of its source value. It is, however, extremely difficult to describe in quantitative terms the decrement of receptor potential with distance in the stretch receptor neurons, for this occurs in a complex of dendritic branches forming a network with the soma and having unknown axial resistances and varying membrane geometry. From the foregoing, it must be evident that impulse activity cannot arise simultaneously in all parts of the cell, since the receptor potential (or its electrotonic derivative) clearly has a varying amplitude along the membrane. In fact, the impulse almost certainly originates in a fairly restricted region of the electrically-excitable membrane. It seems reasonable to assume that this locus would be in the region of the impulse-supporting membrane which is closest to the generator of the receptor potential; for it is in such a region that threshold values of the latter would be reached first. This most certainly would be true if membrane excitability throughout a neuron were everywhere similar, but this is not so. There is now good evidence[45] to indicate that inherent differences in the excitability of the membrane are likely to occur from one part of the cell to the next. Thus, the site of impulse initiation cannot be inherently obvious from the geometry, and attempts to determine its locus on a geometrical basis, seem unwarranted without sound experimental evidence for corroboration.

The measurement of impulse threshold—or firing level—of a sensory neuron by an intracellular electrode is critically dependent not only on the absolute value of depolarization necessary at the site of initiation to trigger the spike, but also on the spatial relationship of the recording pipette to this site. If the recording electrode is inserted directly beneath the membrane region which first generates the impulse, it will of course measure the absolute value of depolarization needed at threshold. If, however, the electrode is spatially removed from the locus of origin of the spike, the depolarization recorded at threshold may be quite a different value. It will be less if the zone of initiation is between the electrode and the source of the receptor potential, and greater if the electrode intervenes between these two regions. In some cases, it may be that the region of electrically-excitable membrane having the lowest threshold is close to, or forms a mosaic with, the electrically-inexcitable membrane which generates the receptor potential. In such cases, the spike-generating mechanism will detect the true magnitude of the receptor potential, since the latter will show no relative degradation by current loss through intervening membrane.

The absorption of stimulus energy in a receptor cell or a primary sensory neuron does not always result in a depolarizing potential change. A graded hyperpolarizing response has been observed, for example, in the blowfly contact chemoreceptor (fig. 13). This effect presumably originates in a single neuron or group of primary sensory neurons. The existence of hyperpolarizing receptor potentials may also be inferred from the results of investigations on primary photosensory neurons in Bivalve molluscs. HARTLINE[47] succeeded in recording activity from the optic nerve of a scallop. This nerve contains two branches, one of which innervates only the sensory neuron population in the distal layer of the retina. This branch was found to produce spontaneous discharge of impulses when the eye was completely dark-adapted.  The response ceased immediately upon re-illumination of the preparation, and the nerve remained electrically silent until the photic energy was removed.  At this point, a transient impulse discharge several times greater than that which occurs in the dark-adapted preparation was recorded. Similar behavior has more recently been shown to occur in single photoreceptor neurons of the surf clam, *Spisula*.[61]  In the latter preparation, an excitatory component also is believed to contribute to the electrical activity of the same cell during illumination, although the gross response of the neuron is similar to that of the nerve supplying the distal retinal layer in the eye of the scallop.

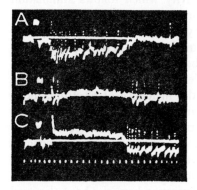

FIG. 13.  Extracellular recordings from a sugar-sensitive neuron in a blowfly chemoreceptor.  (A) Depolarizing receptor potential and a train of action potentials evoked by a solution containing 0·25 M sucrose.  (B) Response to 0·25 M sucrose and 0·05 M calcium chloride.  (C) A hyperpolarizing receptor potential in response to a solution containing 0·05 M calcium chloride.

Note the burst of impulses following removal of the stimulus.  Calibration markers indicate 1 millivolt and 1/60 second.  (From Morita and Yamashita[83], Fig. 2.)

In both instances histological evidence was presented which suggested that the electrical records might represent activity occurring in primary sensory neurons.  If this is the case, it would be justifiable to ascribe the cessation of impulse activity during illumination to a hyperpolarizing receptor potential.  This potential would be capable of inhibiting ongoing impulse activity arising in the neuron in response to intrinsic or other extrinsic influences.  This is the simplest interpretation that can be accorded the data.  This explanation is, however, supported by experimental observations made on a more complex visual system—that of the beetle, *Dytiscus*—by BERNHARD and his colleagues,[15] who found that anodal (hyperpolarizing) currents were effective in inhibiting the discharge which could be recorded from the eye in the dark. Since it has not been possible to obtain intracellular recordings from these interesting types of sensory cells, investigations into the nature of the off-response are incomplete. It might be mentioned that impulse discharges following periods of synaptic inhibition (the so-called 'post-inhibitory rebound' phenomena) are not uncommon among central neurons. In some instances such discharges may be ascribed directly to consequences of the hyperpolarized state, which produces potassium inactivation in the electrically-excitable membrane and results in a period of depolarization as soon as the anodal generator is removed. The excitatory activity which follows stimulation has also been examined using intracellular techniques in other invertebrate primary photosensory neurons (fig. 14). The sequence of electrical events which occurs in these cells appears to be similar to the events described above for predominantly mechanoreceptor neurons.[84] Thus, a depolarizing receptor potential is produced as a consequence of the incidence of electromagnetic energy and is related to stimulus intensity. At a definite threshold amplitude of depolarization, action potentials are generated in electrically excitable regions of the membrane and propagate towards the central nervous system. Where they have been examined, these responses appear to be wavelength-specific.

Transient periods of hyperpolarization have also been observed in the frog muscle spindle[59] after the cessation of a mechanical stimulus. This is shown in figure 15. KATZ regarded these periods of hyperpolarization as part of the 'dynamic' component of the receptor potential—analogous to, but different in electrical sign from, the initial high-amplitude phase of the depolarizing response to passive stretch of the spindle. This phenomenon was noticed also in the intracellular records from crayfish stretch receptors,[27] but was not specifically investigated.

Before examining the control of firing frequency in sensory systems in the next chapter, it may be instructive to consider the terms 'receptor potential' and 'generator potential' as they are used in the experimental literature, since these have engendered some confusion in the past. The functional arrangement of different sensory systems shows a good deal of variation; two basic plans are adhered to, however: (1) the primary sensory neuron,

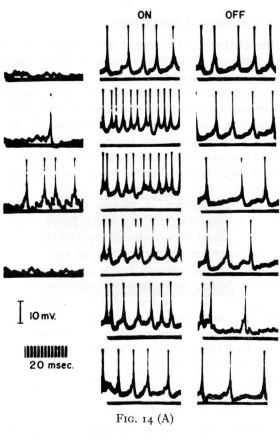

FIG. 14 (A)

FIG. 14 (B)

FIG. 14. (A) Intracellular records from a photosensitive neuron in the sixth abdominal ganglion of the crayfish. In all frames, the lower trace indicates the resting level of internal potential. Light (middle column) evokes a depolarizing receptor potential, and the latter generates impulses.[43] (B) Response to light of a primary photosensory neuron in the eye of a nudibranch mollusc. A large depolarizing receptor potential generates impulses which, from their small size, apparently are not invading the recording site. The calibration markers indicate 50 millivolts and 500 milliseconds. The lower trace is elevated during the light stimulus. (A from Kennedy and Preston,[63] Fig. 7; B from Barth,[10] Fig. 2A.)

37

where different regions of a single nerve cell are concerned with, respectively, the absorption of stimulus energy, the generation of graded slow potential changes, and the initiation of conducted impulses; (2) non-neural sensory cells exhibiting graded activity, and making functional contact with true second-order neurons which initiate conducted impulses. In receptor systems of the latter type there are at least two distinct possible locations for graded electrogenesis—the sensory cell itself, and the region of functional contact between the primary and secondary cells.

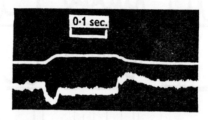

FIG. 15. Extracellular electrical record from a frog stretch receptor. Upper trace indicates duration of applied stretch. Lower trace records the response, which consists of dynamic and steady depolarizing phases (downward deflection) and a brief hyper-polarizing phase following removal of the stimulus. (From Katz,[59] Fig. 1.)

Unless the precise location of an extracellular electrode is known with respect to these two loci, it is difficult to justify positive identification of graded changes in potential due to stimulus application as reflecting particularly either the receptor potential itself or a secondary synaptic potential arising at the junction between the two cells. Without specifying which of these two sources or which combination thereof was involved, BERNHARD, GRANIT and SKOGLAND[16] used the term 'generator potential' to designate the graded depolarization responsible for impulse triggering in the visual system of *Dytiscus*. After its introduction, at which time this term was clearly defined in an operant manner, it appears to have been widely used to designate generally all graded potential changes in receptor systems, often having very little similarity with respect to functional morphology and point of impulse origin. In a review concerning sensory receptor mechanisms which was published in 1961, DAVIS[18] attempted to set standards for the usage of the two terms, in order to clear up some of the ambiguity prevalent within the literature. He proposed that the term 'receptor potential' be used, in the sense first employed by GRAY,[38] to designate the first electrical change in a primary sense cell directly attributable to the absorption of stimulus energy. This concept seems a useful one and is in keeping with the experimental observations. Thus, the receptor potential has a specific causative agent, an absolute magnitude and time-course, and a fixed locus of origin based upon structural modifications and the spatial position of the sensory region of the cell. Moreover, GRAY's definition does not specify (or imply) that the receptor potential necessarily be a depolarization of the membrane.

A 'generator potential' can be any depolarizing potential change which generates conducted impulses. The term is thus ambiguous. DAVIS suggested that it should be used to identify (depolarizing) potential variations in the impulse-generating regions of a sensory system. In primary sensory neurons, this would be identical with the receptor potential and the current sources for both would be the same. In a second-order sensory neuron the generator potential would presumably be equivalent to the depolarizing synaptic (or electrotonic) potential arising across the post-junctional membrane and generating impulses at that point. As discussed above, in some instances the receptor potential may be hyperpolarizing in sign and hardly capable of directly generating action potentials. In other cases, as in the abdominal photoreceptor neurons of crayfish,[60, 62] the cells involved serve as tactile interneurons as well as primary sensory cells for light stimuli. In this preparation conducted impulses are initiated not only in response to light stimuli, but also by conventional postsynaptic potentials evoked as a result of activity in primary mechanosensory neurons. The depolarizations which generate impulses in the abdominal photoreceptor neurons not only may arise from different membrane regions, but also are due to quite different physiological processes. It is thus essential that usage of the term 'generator potential' should be accompanied by adequate qualifications; it should never be assumed by the reader to be synonymous with the receptor potential, unless the anatomical arrangement of the sensory system at hand makes this an obvious conclusion.

## Summary

The events that occur in a primary sensory neuron upon exposure to an adequate stimulus may be summarized as follows. The absorbed stimulus energy (or some fraction of it) effects a change in the resting membrane potential of the cell, a change which is related to stimulus intensity. This change in potential may persist throughout the period of stimulus application and can have either electrical polarity. Since such changes occur in regions of the cell membrane that are electrically-inexcitable, the currents at the source of this receptor potential may be maintained for long periods, although they spread decrementally throughout the neuron; their electrotonic derivative at any point decreases with distance and is critically dependent upon membrane geometry. If a region of low-threshold electrically-excitable membrane is sufficiently close to the source of a depolarizing receptor potential, or in any case, if the electrotonic potential is of sufficient amplitude, impulses may be initiated throughout the period of time during which the depolarized state exceeds the threshold amplitude. The nature of the control of impulse frequency by such supra-threshold depolarizations will be examined in the next chapter.

# 3 : The Control of Impulse Frequency

In the last chapter we have seen that special regions of sensory neurons are adapted for the generation of maintained electrical changes when acted on by a stimulus.  It is usually assumed that the intensity and dynamic parameters of a stimulus are encoded in the frequency of impulses which reach the central nervous system, and these latter are in fact dependent upon mechanisms at the nerve-ending.  Yet, in spite of its obvious importance as a physiological phenomenon, the control of impulse frequency in sensory neurons has not received the experimental attention it deserves.  This is especially surprising in view of the advantages which have been gained by the development of intracellular electrodes.  Only a few preparations have been examined extensively with the purpose of elucidating the relationship between the slow potential changes and the frequency of the resulting impulse train evoked by a particular stimulus.  These investigations have, however, emphasized the complexity of the frequency control process and the present limitations in our comprehension of its operation.

In primary sensory neurons the frequency of propagated action potentials is critically dependent upon the magnitude of the receptor potential elicited by the stimulus.  KATZ, working with the frog muscle spindle, was the first to make quantitative measurements of this relationship[59] and he showed that a plot of impulse frequency versus receptor potential magnitude was essentially linear.  Similar measurements have now been made for at least three other sensory neurons, revealing the same relationship (see fig. 22).  Nevertheless, a simple explanation of this relationship in terms of the known properties of the nerve membrane is not immediately obvious.

If an outward current is caused to flow across an area of electrically-excitable membrane (either from an instrumental source or from a region of the cell generating a receptor current), the potential difference across the membrane will at first change with time in an exponential fashion. The final value attained will be dictated by the effective transmembrane resistance and the density of the current flowing across it. The time course of these changes will be determined by the product of membrane resistance and capacitance. However, membrane impedance $(R \times C)$ is known to undergo dramatic changes during an action potential: the action currents during the spike first effecting a large depolarizing overshoot; this is followed, as has been explained on page 8, by a repolarization, which may reach the potassium equilibrium potential, even in the face of a sustained depolarizing influence. As the membrane impedance returns to its resting values, the depolarizing generator currents once more effect an exponentially rising change in the $IR$ drop across the membrane. In the absence of other factors (such as changes in impulse threshold and development of a local membrane response) spike frequency at any level of depolarization would depend on the membrane time-constant, for it is this factor that governs the rate of change of membrane depolarization following recovery from each action potential. ' Other factors ', however, cannot be ignored; at least two additional properties associated with electrically-excitable membranes complicate the process of frequency control. As HODGKIN[50] first discovered in 1938, impulse threshold is attained, not by passive depolarization of the membrane (appearing as an $IR$ drop due to extrinsically generated currents), but only after the development of a local sub-threshold response. This response is initiated by levels of membrane depolarization lower than those required to trigger a full action potential. Two wholly independent properties of the membrane thus jointly determine the rate at which a depolarizing influence arrives at threshold levels for impulse-initiation. The situation is diagramatically illustrated in figure 16. In addition to those factors which affect the rate of change in membrane potential of electrically-excitable tissue, the impulse threshold itself undergoes changes in value during and following each spike. Such changes in excitability delineate the relative and absolute refractory periods that occur in impulse-generating

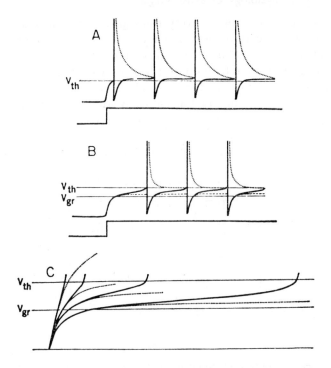

FIG. 16. Diagram to illustrate the possible ways in which the membrane potential changes with time after the application of a steady depolarizing current. (A) (hypothetical) No local membrane response is triggered; potential rises to level of spike threshold ($V_{th}$) along an exponential curve dictated solely by the membrane time constant. The first and succeeding impulse intervals are longer than the interval between stimulus onset and the first spike, since membrane refractoriness (dotted line) raises impulse threshold following each transient. (B) As first shown by Hodgkin, impulse threshold is reached by the growth of a local or graded membrane response, the threshold for which is indicated by the line $V_{gr}$. Following an instantaneous onset of constant current, the membrane potential at first changes in an exponential fashion until it reaches $V_{gr}$. The local response then brings the level to impulse threshold. If membrane refractoriness is brief, no interference with membrane excitation occurs, and succeeding spike intervals are identical with the interval between stimulus onset and the first spike. (C) Differences between membrane potential changes occasioned by purely passive electrical characteristics (dotted lines), and a combination of passive and active factors (solid lines). Responses to four different levels of stimulating current are shown. (From Fuortes and Mantegazzini,[33] Fig. 1.)

43

membrane during the recovery from an action potential. One theory of the control of frequency in sensory receptors, propounded by ADRIAN[2] in 1928, utilized the continuously changing state of membrane refractoriness (during recovery) to account for recurrent excitation in the face of a constantly maintained stimulus. ADRIAN supposed that a steady stimulus might re-excite a sensory neuron, so that another impulse could be initiated as soon as the absolute refractory period of the preceding spike had passed. As is illustrated in figure 17, the strongest stimuli (being

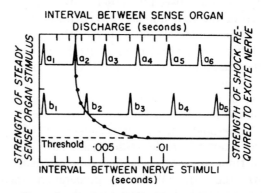

FIG. 17. Control of impulse frequency solely by membrane refractory period, as first proposed by Adrian. Impulse threshold is infinite during the absolute refractory period, and thereafter it falls with time as indicated by the curved line. Greater levels of stimulating current will thus trigger successive impulses earlier in the refractory period than will weak ones. As indicated, an *a*-level shock or stimulus will generate a higher frequency of impulses than one at *b*-level. (From Adrian,[2] Fig. 10.)

able to excite less sensitive membrane) would trigger successive impulses early in the relative refractory period, whereas a weaker stimulus would require longer periods of recovery between spikes. Re-excitation would thus only occur after longer intervals of time. A serious criticism of the 'refractory period hypothesis' arises from the finding that some neurons fire rhythmically at impulse frequencies a good deal lower than those which would necessarily be dictated by the duration of their relative refractory periods. This point was emphasized by HODGKIN[51] in studies of a sense organ model. Utilizing the large single motor axons available in the peripheral nerves of the limbs of crabs, HODGKIN examined the relationship between strength of a steady depolarizing current and impulse frequency, and between the average impulse interval and the interval required after stimulus onset to produce the first spike.  About half the fibers used in the experimental procedure adapted rather quickly to a steady depolarization, so that inter-spike interval increased continuously as a function of time.  The remaining fibers, however, gave prolonged and extremely regular discharges in response to a steady depolarizing current.  In these latter cells, the interval between the onset of stimulus current and the appearance of the first impulse was identical with that for succeeding interspike intervals—except when the current strength was very high (fig. 18).  These results have been interpreted as indicating the importance of sub-threshold or local response development in determining the duration of impulse interval.  There is now, in fact, wide acceptance of the contribution to frequency control in many sense organs made by the rate of growth of sub-threshold activity.  Experimental results verifying the data from HODGKIN's model sense organs have, for example, been obtained from the slowly-adapting stretch-sensitive neuron in the crayfish (fig. 19).  With this preparation, increase in stimulus intensity (applied by stretching the receptor muscle) resulted in a corresponding rise in the prepotential which occurred in advance of successive impulses.  The time taken to attain impulse threshold decreased, therefore, primarily as a result of the rate of increase of the local response.

With stimuli of very large intensities, which produce relatively high impulse frequencies, the membrane refractory period cer-tainly influences interspike interval, both in the model sense-organ studied by HODGKIN and in primary sensory neurons them-selves.  This effect is illustrated graphically in figure 20, where the deviation of the initial response time from that of discharge interval may be clearly seen at the higher stimulus strengths.  In figure 19, the influence of the refractory period in deter-mining the firing frequency of the slowly-adapting stretch-sensitive neuron of the crayfish is indicated by the change in firing level traced by the broken line.  Thus, when a slowly-adapting neuron is confronted with an unvarying depolarization, the impulse frequency is determined both by rate of development of

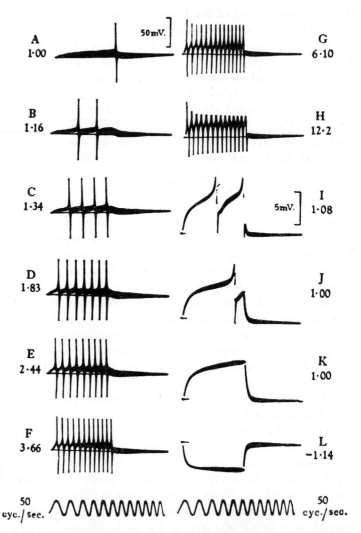

FIG. 18. Extracellular recordings obtained by Hodgkin from a single motor axon of a crab in response to constant current steps of 100 milliseconds' duration. The numbers beneath index letters indicate relative current strengths. Except at very high current intensities (e.g. H) successive impulse intervals are all identical with that interval of time between the onset of the stimulating current and the appearance of the first spike. (From Hodgkin,[51] Fig. 1.)

46

the local response, and—especially at high stimulus intensities—
by the relative refractory period of the impulse-initiating regions
of the cell membrane.    There appear to be great differences
between neurons with respect to the relative stability of both of
these processes during activity.    In many nerve cells, including

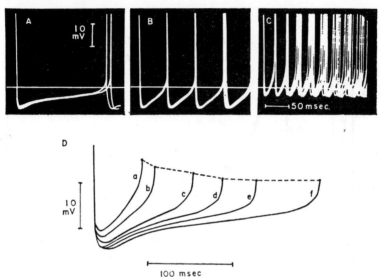

FIG. 19.    Intracellular records from a slowly-adapting crustacean stretch
receptor sensory neuron showing changes in the slope of the graded
responses with an increase in amplitude of the receptor potential (A-D),
and indicating an increase in the impulse threshold (height of dotted line
in D) at high frequencies.    (From Eyzaguirre and Kuffler,[27] Fig. 6.)

some primary sensory neurons, the properties of the active
membrane change during prolonged periods of excitation.    This
results in accommodation and accumulated refractoriness, two
factors which effect neuron output;  the former slows down the
rate of rise of successive local responses, even though the level of
depolarization generating the impulses may remain constant, so
that the threshold for triggering will be attained after successively
greater increments of time following a spike;  and the latter
increases the firing threshold from the lower values obtaining at
the onset of the stimulus.    Both these processes occur in electrically-excitable membrane regions.    FUORTES and MANTEGAZZINI[33]

have examined the operation of these independent factors, which tend to lessen the steady response of the neural membrane, in the eccentric cells of the *Limulus* compound eye. They have shown that prolonged depolarizations, induced by passing outward current across the neural membrane, produce impulse trains

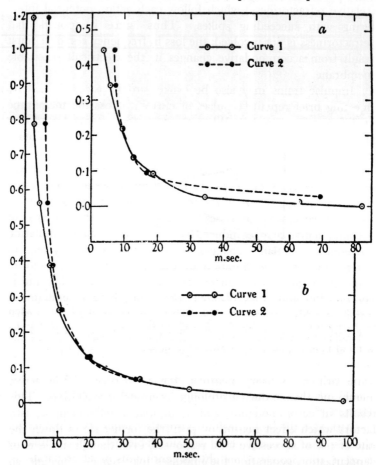

FIG. 20.   Data from two experiments on single isolated crab nerve fibers showing the increasing discrepancy at high stimulus-strengths between the interval between first and second spikes of a train (filled circles) and the interval between current onset and the first spike (open circles).   The ordinate is relative current strength.   (From Hodgkin,[51] Fig. 3.)

which are initiated after shorter intervals of time than those separating the first, second, etc., impulses. Successive impulse intervals, moreover, tend to increase as a function of time. This behavior is especially obvious at low stimulus intensities (fig. 21), where there can be little possibility of the recovery processes (relative refractoriness) which follow each action potential interfering with succeeding spikes. Thus, since it appears that refractoriness is not involved, the loss in frequency response must result from accommodative changes in the electrically-excitable membrane.

Impulse trains may also be evoked in the eccentric cell by injecting brief repetitive pulses of current across the membrane at different frequencies. When this was done, it was found that smaller total quantities of electric charge were needed to maintain comparable spike frequencies than when a steady current was used. None the less, a gradual increase in impulse interval was also observed with this mode of stimulation. This was manifested by the increasing failure of the stimuli in the later parts of a train to evoke successive impulses. Thus, even in the absence of accommodative changes induced by prolonged constant stimulating currents, accumulative changes in membrane excitability tend to extend the effective duration of the refractory period and to prolong the interval of reduced sensitivity following each impulse. As FUORTES and MANTEGAZZINI point out, little is understood either of refractoriness or accommodation other than ' . . . that the first is an unknown process brought about by firing and the second is an equally unknown process due to the stimulus '. To date, it does not appear that either process can be adequately explained on the basis of known parameters in the mathematical model of the axonal membrane proposed by HODGKIN and HUXLEY.[52]

Although the initial decline in impulse frequency characterizes the response of many nerve cells to stable levels of stimulating current, this process is not always continuous in all preparations; for a steady impulse frequency is often approached and maintained following an initial-frequency decline. During such a steady phase of firing the impulse frequency tends to be linearly related to membrane depolarization, as was first observed by KATZ[59] and later confirmed for other primary and secondary sensory neurons (fig. 22). This apparently simple relationship between membrane potential and firing frequency is particularly difficult to explain on quantitative grounds. Some of HODGKIN's earliest studies demonstrated that the rate of rise of the local response is an exponential function of membrane depolarization. Since firing frequency in many nerve cells is controlled to a large extent by the growth of the local response after each impulse has repolarized the membrane, it follows that spike frequency should itself increase exponentially as the generator potential increases in

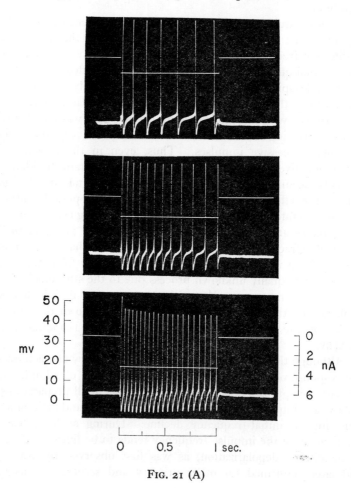

FIG. 21 (A)

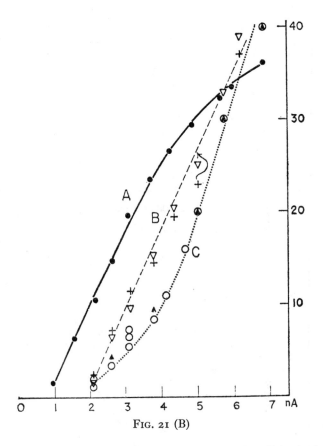

Fig. 21 (B)

Fig. 21. (A) Intracellular records from an eccentric cell in the lateral eye of *Limulus*. The three traces illustrate the response of the cell to increasing strengths of current passed through the recording electrode. (B) Impulse frequency plotted against stimulus intensity for (A) current steps 1 sec. long, (B) trains of pulses of 7 msec. duration and recurring at 40/sec., (C) trains of pulses of 7 msec. duration and recurring at different frequencies. Ordinate and abscissa in (A) and (B) indicate impulse frequency and current intensity, respectively. In (C) the ordinate again indicates impulse (=pulse) frequency; the abscissa indicates the strength of current required to give a complete train of impulses. (A from Fuortes,[31] Fig. 9.)

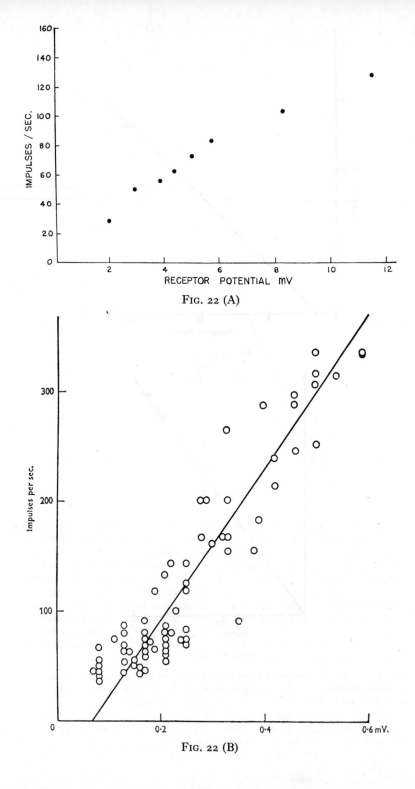

FIG. 22 (A)

FIG. 22 (B)

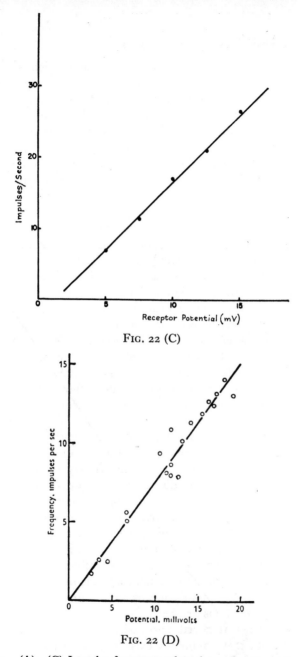

FIG. 22 (C)

FIG. 22 (D)

FIG. 22. (A) – (C) Impulse frequency plotted as a function of receptor potential amplitude. (A) An insect mechanosensory sensillum.[103] (B) A muscle spindle of the frog.[59] (C) A crayfish abdominal stretch receptor neuron (plotted from data given in Terzuolo and Washizu.[96] In (D) impulse frequency is plotted against the amplitude of the generator potential recorded from an eccentric cell in the lateral eye of *Limulus*. (A from Wolbarsht,[103] Fig. 2; B from Katz,[59] Fig. 2B; D from MacNichol,[74] Fig. 8.)

amplitude, and not in the simple linear fashion which is actually observed. This apparent contradiction might be explained by increases in the length of the refractory period, which indeed have been shown to occur at higher impulse frequencies. Such an effect might counteract the tendency of a neuron to reach the firing threshold at larger depolarizations. At the present time, however, any attempt to explain the linear relationship must be purely speculative, for there is no coherent experimental evidence which bears on this question.

An additional influence on impulse frequency control in primary sensory neurons may occur because of variations in stimulus-evoked depolarization, for it is unlikely that a naturally-induced receptor potential would have a rectangular waveform. Adaptation, therefore, may be as much the result of a decay in amplitude of the receptor potential as it is of processes occurring in the electrically-excitable membrane regions. In particular, many primary mechanoreceptor neurons are maximally sensitive to movement rather than static displacement, and the receptor potential set up by transient excursions of the end organ rapidly decay when the velocity of the excursions declines. Thus, KATZ observed a dynamic phase of the receptor potential in the frog muscle spindle, in response to sudden stretching of the organ. More characteristically phasic responses may be obtained from the Pacinian corpuscle[72] and some insect movement receptors.[103] There is no reason to suppose that the factors responsible for adaptation of the receptor potential in primary sensory cells are any less complicated and diverse than those involved in the gradual reduction of activity occurring in electrically-excitable membranes. The loss of effective energy absorption, and/or its transfer to electrogenic mechanisms within the cell, might operate to diminish the magnitude of the slow electrical response by a stimulus of unvarying strength. This problem has now been directly investigated in the Pacinian corpuscle by MENDELSON and LOEWENSTEIN.[82, 72] In this mechanoreceptor, a single sensory nerve-ending functions as the receptive element. The endings may be found and removed most easily from mammalian visceral mesentery, but they commonly exist in other parts of the body, including the joints and skin. A diagram of the sensory structure may be seen in figure 23. Most noticeable is the heavy capsule

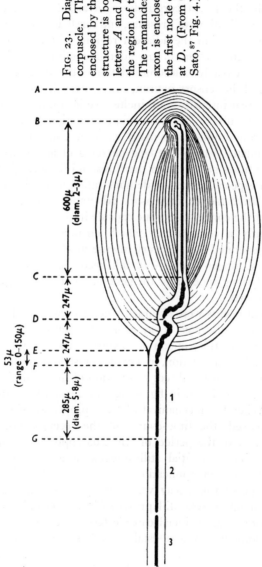

FIG. 23. Diagram of a Pacinian corpuscle. The region normally enclosed by the capsular structure is bounded by the letters *A* and *E*. *B-C* indicates the region of the nerve-ending. The remainder of the sensory axon is enclosed by myelin, and the first node of Ranvier occurs at *D*. (From Quilliam and Sato,[87] Fig. 4.)

of connective tissue in which the ending itself is imbedded. Earlier work has shown that mechanical deformations applied to the capsule are transmitted to the nerve-ending, where they produce a graded receptor potential which varies in amplitude as a function of stimulus intensity. However, the duration of the receptor potential in the intact corpuscle is invariably brief, even with prolonged applications of pressure, and rarely is more than a single impulse generated in the adjacent regions of the axon following the sudden application of an adequate stimulus. This brief response is due partly to accommodation of the impulse-generating membrane of the sensory neuron, since externally applied currents —even of great intensity—are ineffective in producing more than a very few impulses. Indeed, in six preparations so tested, only a single neuron produced as many as three consecutive impulses when stimulated with prolonged currents of an intensity which was twelve times greater than the threshold for a single impulse ! This is an especially striking demonstration of the importance of accommodative factors in sensory adaptation. In addition, the presence of the connective tissue capsule in the Pacinian corpuscle is apparently a construction which ensures that the receptor potential generated even by very intense mechanical deformations will not last longer than 6 – 10 milliseconds, a period which is usually only long enough for the generation of a single propagated action potential.

Different results were obtained when the capsule of a Pacinian corpuscle was dissected away from the sensory nerve-ending itself.[71] Since this operation exposes the nerve-ending to experimental manipulation, it enables observations to be made upon the effects of the direct application of mechanical energy to the ending. As shown in figure 24, the results were quite conclusive. When the mechanical filtering properties of the capsule were by-passed, the time-course of the receptor potential reproduced that of the period of stimulus application much more faithfully. The potential still underwent a continuous decay following the sudden application of pressure to the naked ending, but the slope of this decay was greatly reduced and a discernible depolarization was still present 60 milliseconds afterwards. Furthermore, if an artificial capsule (composed of several layers of thin mesothelium) was re-established between the nerve-ending and the stimulus source, the response to prolonged deformations was considerably shorter than when they were applied directly to the nerve-ending itself. It therefore seems reasonable to conclude that a major factor in the adaptation process of the Pacinian corpuscle is the mechanical filtering characteristic of the

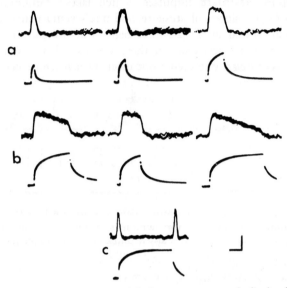

Fig. 24. Receptor potentials (upper traces, $a-c$) obtained in response to mechanical pulses of varying duration (monitored on bottom trace) from a Pacinian corpuscle. The responses in rows $a$ and $b$ were obtained after the capsule had been dissected away from the nerve-ending. The response in $c$ was obtained from the intact receptor. Calibration pulses: 10 msec. and 50 $\mu$V. (From Loewenstein and Mendelson,[72] Fig. 2.)

capsule, which couples the stimulus to the sensory cell. This latter principle is of some importance, for, regardless of the rapid accommodation which characterizes the sensory axon, a large part of the initial decline in the ability of the receptor to respond repetitively clearly occurs as a result of the effective removal of the stimulus at the level of mechano-electric conversion, even though the outer layers of the capsule itself may still be exposed to it.

Some additional support for the role of mechanical factors in adaptation comes from work on the mammalian muscle spindle.[67]

S.O.—E

These investigations indicated that the higher frequency of impulse discharge seen at the onset of a mechanical stimulus, or during a step-wise increase in stimulus strength, is due to phasic response characteristics of the receptor potential. Steady depolarizing currents applied to the sense organ produced stable, non-adapting trains of impulses, which lasted throughout the duration of the electrical stimulus. Thus, strictly neural factors (such as accommodation and increased refractoriness) are apparently of small consequence in these organs. High-gain extracellular recordings, obtained from electrodes placed close to the

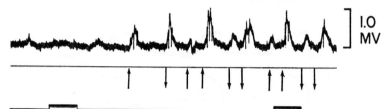

FIG. 25. Depolarizing receptor potentials (upward deflections) and impulses evoked in an associated sensory neurone by displacing an insect cuticular hair. The arrows indicate the approximate time of onset of each stimulus and the direction of movement with respect to the preceding one. Time marks recur every 200 milliseconds. (From Wolbarsht,[103] Fig. 8.)

insertion of the sensory nerve in the muscle, showed an unmistakable phasic (' dynamic ') component early in the waveform of the receptor potential similar to those seen by KATZ in the muscle spindle of the frog (cf. fig. 15). Thus, there can be little doubt that the major adaptive process in the muscle spindle of vertebrates involves a decline in receptor potential amplitude, and this, in turn, probably results from a mechanical uncoupling at the level of the insertion of the sensory nerve-endings into the receptor organs. Other examples also can be cited, such as the mechano-sensory neurons associated with trichoid sensilla in various insects.[103] As shown in figure 25, records of the receptor potential waveform from these cells, obtained during mechanical stimulation of the organ, indicate once again that, in rapidly adapting cells (such as those which respond only to movement), the first component of sensory adaptation is a decline in the amplitude of the receptor potential. In so-called 'position' sense organs, on the other hand, the receptor potential is maintained during displacement of the sense organ from some 'resting' position, and impulse frequency appears to be a linear function of receptor potential amplitude.

No discussion of mechanoreceptor adaptation would be complete without an examination of the classic examples of slowly- and rapidly-adapting neurons associated with the crayfish abdominal stretch-receptors. The relationship between the time-course of the receptor potential and the duration of the applied stimulus has been examined in the slowly-adapting organ by FLOREY.[29] It was found that both the onset and the cessation of stimuli were followed by dynamic phases in the time-course of the receptor potential, while the major portion of the response was characteristically steady. The situation in the rapidly-adapting stretch-receptor neuron was found to be different.[65, 101] The receptor potential in this cell is independent of the duration of the applied stimulus, and it decays with a characteristic time-course after onset of the stretch, possibly due to in-series visco-elastic elements at the insertion of the dendrites into the receptor muscle. Neural adaptation is also pronounced,[85] as has been found to occur in the Pacinian corpuscle. Thus, the physiological characteristics of both the transducer and the spike-generating regions of these two sensory cells seem to complement one another. One other example may be appropriately mentioned at this point to indicate the potential importance of the site for mechano-electric conversion as a potential locus for sensory adaptation. In the dually-innervated tactile hairs found on the crayfish thorax,[77] the rate of sensory adaptation to equivalent deflections of the hair may show great differences between the two neurons. When exposed to a constant source of cathodal current, however, the same two cells adapt at nearly identical rates.

Adaptation at the non-nervous level is a prominent feature of many primary photoreceptor cells. Although these cells in various arthropod preparations have axons which run to the central nervous system, there is some evidence that no impulses are generated or propagated in these structures. Electrical recordings made from the retinula cells of many insects and crustaceans, and from *Limulus*, disclose only a receptor potential which is evoked by light energy of various wavelengths. Although both the amplitude and duration of the major part of this depolarization are functions of light intensity, a large peak is prominent at the beginning of such records (especially when the stimulus intensity is great), and this phase of the electrical response decays at a rate which is independent of the stimulus (fig. 26). At the present time there is no clue as to the specific nature of this initial, rapidly-declining phase of the receptor potential. The situation is complicated by the fact that, in some related preparations, this part of the response can attain great amplitudes—often over-shooting the zero level of potential—while its duration can become quite brief. This response thus has some of the characteristics of a regenerative spike, although it is apparently not propagated along the nerve. A report of a non-propagated electrically-excitable component of the receptor potential in the *Limulus* eye has, in fact, recently appeared.[13] It is possible that the response illustrated in figure 26 has a similar physiological basis. Further studies may establish these rapid components as an entirely new response mechanism peculiar to visual receptors.

Large gaps exist in our knowledge of the excitatory train of events which occur in photoreceptor cells following the absorption of light. In all photoreceptors the initial event involves the utilization of specific wavelengths to isomerize a photolabile pigment; it is generally thought that the chemical properties of pigments in different sensory cells determine which of the available energy spectrum will be most effective in the process of photo-isomerization, and this is now known to be the physical basis for color vision.[75] Pigments from different animal groups differ in the minor details of chemical structure; however, a protein-carotenoid molecular complex appears to be invariably involved, whether the animal is a crayfish or a cow, and thus many of the specific chemical details in the detection of light can be generalized.

In man, the visual pigment subserving night-time, or scotopic, vision is located in the outer segments of the retinal sensory cells known as rods. The pigment complement of these cells, rhodopsin, is a complex of a specific protein and a carotenoid—a derivative of vitamin A. The protein, opsin, and the carotenoid, neo-b retinal, can exist in a conjugated state only in the dark. Electro-magnetic energy, especially in the wavelength band of $400 - 600 \mu$,

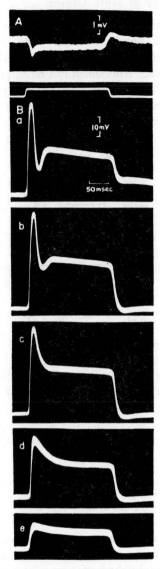

FIG. 26. Response of a blowfly retinula cell to light. (A) Electrical record obtained by extracellular recording from the cell. (B) Intracellular records obtained in response to lights of decreasing intensity, *a–e*. Duration of the stimulus is indicated by the elevated region of the upper trace in *a*. (From Washizu,[98] Fig. 1.)

isomerizes the retinal from an 11-cis to an all-trans configuration, and the chemical bonds necessary for the retinal-protein complex are thereby sterically hindered; thus, the pigment integrity is destroyed. Rhodopsin can be resynthesized following the initial photochemical reaction by alternative mechanisms (fig. 27). The most direct of these involves an enzymatic isomerization of all-trans retinene to the neo-b configuration, and

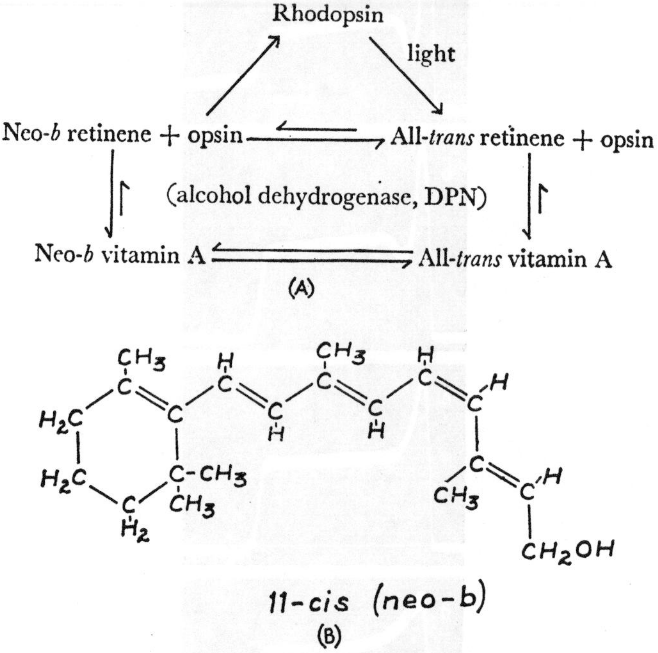

FIG. 27. (A) Scheme indicating the reactions involved in the breakdown and synthesis of rhodopsin. (B) Chemical structure of neo-b retinene. (B from Wald,[97] Fig. 5.)

this substance can spontaneously combine with available opsin. Alternatively, all-trans retinene is reduced to all-trans vitamin A by the enzyme, alcohol dehydrogenase. The vitamin A isomer is then isomerized to the neo-b (11-cis) configuration, and the product of this reaction is oxidized to the active form of retinene.[21]

The loss in visual acuity following exposure to a very strong light has been attributed to the photic breakdown of available visual pigment. Indeed, it has now been shown that the rate of reconstitution of visual pigment *in vitro*[21, 97] as well as *in vivo*[92, 93] parallels very closely the recovery of visual sensitivity (fig. 28). Nevertheless, the loss in visual sensitivity occasioned by exposure to rather weak light cannot be entirely explained on the basis of simple chemical kinetics;  thus, neural adaptation cannot be ruled out as a contributing factor.

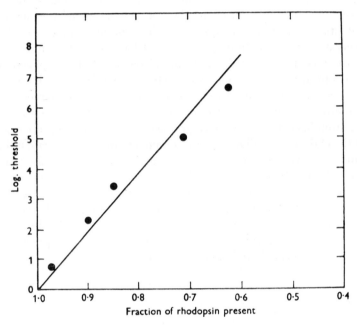

FIG. 28.   The logarithm of visual threshold (o = the threshold for the dark-adapted eye) plotted as a function of available rhodopsin within the receptor cells.   Data were obtained from the living human eye.   (From Rushton,[93] Fig. 3.)

## Summary

The control of impulse frequency in primary sensory neurons is complex.   It can involve changes in the responsiveness of the spike-initiating regions of the membrane to extrinsic currents, not only in regard to the rate of rise of local sub-threshold responses, but also in the threshold for full impulse generation.  In slowly-adapting cells these changes, if they occur, stabilize with time, so that a steady rate of firing can persist during most of the time that the stimulus is applied to the sense organ.  The impulse frequency during this period is usually related to the amplitude of the receptor potential in a linear manner.  It follows from this that the logarithmic relationship which is often observed between the stimulus and the impulse frequency must result from a transformation at a step prior to that of generation of the action potential (i.e. in the coupling of the stimulus energy to the generator of the receptor potential).  Changes in the amplitude of the receptor potential can occur subsequent to the application of a constant stimulus, with predictable consequences for impulse frequency.  In some mechanoreceptors, this degradation in amplitude results from an uncoupling of the nerve-ending from the stimulus energy, as a consequence of the mechanical properties of the end-organ.  Thus, a large component of sensory adaptation can be mechanical in origin.  Non-neural adaptation can also play a significant role in governing the response of other types of sense organs, for example in primary photoreceptor cells.  The decreases in the amplitude of the receptor potential with time which may be seen in these cells may result partially from the bleaching of available visual pigment; but other, less understood, processes also are implicated, and they may be no less important.

# 4 : Origins of the Receptor Potential

In Chapter 2 evidence was advanced which indicates that the receptor potential is generated in areas of the sensory cell membrane which are electrically inexcitable and are, therefore, physiologically different from regions which support regenerative electrical activity. Time-dependent processes in the electrogenic membrane, for example, are of little importance in determining the waveform of the receptor potential. The changes in membrane permeability which are responsible for its generation are, in fact, maintained throughout the period that the stimulus is energetically bound to the sensory membrane. Secondary uncoupling of stimulus energy from the sensory cell can occur, as was discussed in the preceding chapter, although this seems to be largely a function of the accessory structures alone. This latter process thus occurs at functional levels in the sensory process which are separate from changes in permeability of the cellular membrane.

The receptor potential which occurs in a primary sensory neuron or a sensory cell is an $IR$ drop which is generated by current flow through the electrical resistance of inactive membrane regions. This latter current results from the movement of ions through loci where the resting permeability of the membrane has been altered by the transduction of stimulus energy.*

This chapter will be devoted to a review of the evidence that (1) the absorption of stimulus energy leads to a decreased membrane resistance, resulting in the inward flow of ionic current,

---

* The conventions which define the electrical polarity of these changes are similar to those used with regard to electrically-excitable membrane; thus, the current due to an inward movement of positive ions at the transducer locus will cross adjacent membrane regions in an outward direction, thereby discharging the membrane capacitance and depolarizing the cell.

and (2) the major external ion species involved in depolarizing receptor potentials is sodium.

An increase in membrane permeability for diffusible ion species (= increased membrane conductance) can most easily be detected as a decrease in the overall electrical resistance of the sensory cell membrane. A thorough investigation of such resistance changes has been made by FUORTES[31] for the case of the eccentric cell in the eye of *Limulus* following exposure to light. While this preparation is not a primary sense cell, there is a good deal of justification for assuming that the principles involved in the production of the generator potentials in this eye are similar to those responsible for other stimulus-induced potential changes found in alternative sensory arrangements.

It is not usually practical to make a direct measurement of ionic current flow across the sensory cell membrane during stimulation, although this would be the most satisfactory means of determining the magnitude of increased membrane conductance. Usually it is simpler to measure changes in overall membrane resistance by recording the alterations which occur when a potential drop is generated by passing a known constant current across the membrane. The potential of the resting membrane is, of course, changed by the passage of such a current, and this voltage should summate with a receptor potential induced by the stimulus. In the *Limulus* eye, for example, light energy causes a depolarization, and an artificially generated potential can summate with it to produce impulses if the total depolarization surpasses threshold values. In fact, any supra-threshold combination of light and artificially-evoked decrease in resting potential will generate equivalent impulse frequencies, so long as the absolute level of membrane potential reached in all cases is the same. However, as shown in figure 29, FUORTES found that the relationship between experimentally applied depolarizing current and the voltage drop generated by such current itself changes with different values of stimulus light intensity, and the change is steepest—with maximum slope—in the dark. Since the slope of the relationship is equal to $E/I = R$, that is, overall membrane resistance, it can be seen that this parameter decreases as light intensity is increased. The conclusion drawn is that the end result of stimulating the eye with light is an increased conductance

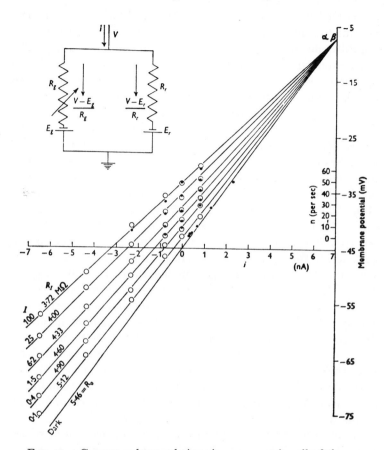

FIG. 29.    Current-voltage relations in an eccentric cell of the eye of *Limulus*.    The slope of each curve is equal to the electrical resistance of the cell membrane in the immediate neighborhood of the measuring electrode.    This value changes when light of different intensities is shone on the eye.    Open circles represent voltages obtained by different strengths of current at the various levels of illumination.    The small closed circles indicate parallel relationships between impulse frequency and current.    *Abscissa* : current passed across the cell membrane, in amperes × $10^{-9}$.    *Ordinate*: membrane potential (mV) and impulse frequency (n).

    *Inset*    An electrical model of the eccentric cell membrane.    A complete description is given in the text.    (From Rushton,[90] Figs. 4 and 4*A*.)

of part of the eccentric cell membrane, allowing inward ionic current to flow, which moves outwards in adjacent regions and critically depolarizes spike-generating membrane parts. The exact proportion of eccentric cell membrane involved with the light-induced resistance changes has so far been impossible to calculate, but it is thought to include most of the distal process of the neuron (rhabdom) which is surrounded by the primary sensory cells. It is important to note in figure 29 that, since the current-voltage curves are linear over the ranges tested, current *per se* has little direct influence upon membrane resistance. The membrane is electrically inexcitable, and some other agent, possibly chemical, which is released as a result of the absorption of light, appears to be involved. The equivalent circuit figured in the inset of figure 29 also implies that there is a functional differentiation of the eccentric cell membrane. In this circuit the membrane batteries, $E_g$ and $E_r$, are assumed to be identical in the unstimulated state, and the internal resistance coupling the two membrane types is ignored. The resistance of the sensory membrane, $R_g$, is variable and is related to light intensity, so that a decrease from its resting value will cause current to flow in the circuit in such a direction as to reduce the e.m.f. of the resting membrane.

Results similar to those described above were obtained by FUORTES[32] several years later from primary sensory cells in the eye of the dragonfly. Thus, it seems probable that changes in membrane conductance may be a universal consequence of photochemical reactions in light-sensitive structures.

WOLBARSHT[103] was the first to provide evidence that increases in conductance follows stimulus-application in primary mechanosensory neurons. Using the tactile sensilla of various insects, he showed that there is a linear relationship between impulse frequency and the amplitude of the receptor potential produced by translational displacement of the sensory structures. In addition, however, he found a linear relationship between the receptor potential and the amplitude of the resulting nerve impulses: At maximum stimulus intensities, impulse height also attained its greatest values (fig. 30). To understand this, it is necessary to examine the rather unique method used to record the electrical activity of neurons associated with these insect sensilla. Each of these hair-like structures contains two inner canals, and

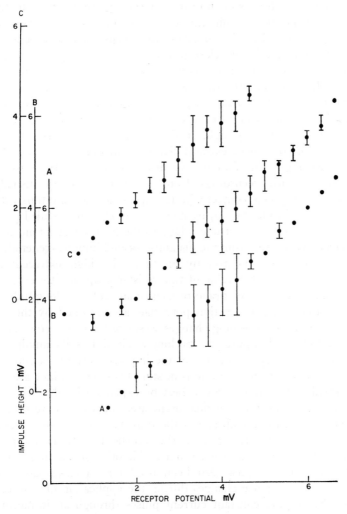

FIG. 30. The relationship between impulse height and receptor potential amplitude in three different insect mechanosensory neurons, measured by a recording pipette placed over the tip of a sensillum. The change in impulse amplitude is thought to be due to an increase in the conductance of the neuronal membrane beneath the recording electrode. (From Wolbarsht,[103] Fig. 9.)

at least one of these is open to the external environment at the tip of the sensillum.  Within this canal are the distal processes of sensory nerve cells.  The somata of these cells are located beneath the cuticle of the insect, close to the base of the sensillum.  The distal processes of the neurons must thus traverse the articulation at the base of the structure, and at this point the inner canal through which they run is highly constricted.  As a result, the electrical resistance of the canal between the base and the tip of the sensillum is extremely high, due to the very small cross-sectional area of the column of extracellular fluid in this region and the close packing of the four or five distal processes of the sensory neurons.  Now recordings from these neurons are usually obtained by making contact with the tip of the hair (and thus with the neurons inside the tip) by means of an electrolyte-filled glass capillary recording electrode.  Due to the basal constriction, this electrode is isolated from the distantly-located impulse-generating membrane of the neuron by an unusually high extracellular resistance.  Since the value of this resistance apparently exceeds the combined cell membrane resistance and internal longitudinal axoplasmic resistance, action potentials are recorded by the tip electrode as positive-going changes, as suggested by the equivalent circuit detailed in figure 31.  So long as absolute spike amplitude and locus of closest approach of the impulse to the tip electrode do not change during variations in stimulus strength, increases in recorded spike amplitude can best be explained by decreases in the electrical resistance of membrane areas beneath the recording electrode, i.e. the membrane of the transducer region of the cell.

It is not surprising that the crustacean stretch-receptor preparation, which has proved so useful in other studies of sensory neuron properties, has also been used for an examination of membrane-resistance changes during the application of a stimulus.  By passing constant current pulses through an intracellular recording pipette, evidence has been provided[96] that such changes also occur as a direct result of the absorption of stimulus energy in these sensory neurons.  Conclusive evidence is therefore available from several sensory systems that the immediate consequence of stimulus application is an increase in the ionic conductance of the sense cell membrane.  The amplitude and time-course of these conductance changes are also directly controlled by the stimulus. Normally, these changes result in an inward current flow at the sensor locus, due to a movement of one or more ion species moving down their electrochemical gradients, which causes a depolarization of the resting membrane in adjacent regions of the cell. It is probable that hyperpolarizing receptor potentials also exist, although these would most certainly

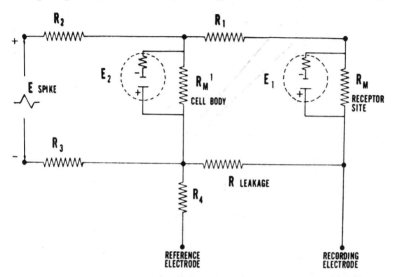

FIG. 31. An electrical model of the insect mechanosensory neuron and the recording situation. The recording pipette is separated from the impulse-supporting membrane by an extremely large external resistance ($R$ leakage), by the membrane resistance ($R_M$), and by the internal longitudinal resistance of the distal process of the sensory neuron ($R_1$). The amplitude and polarity of action potentials ($E$ spike) depend upon the ratio of the resistances, $R_M/R$ Leakage. When this ratio becomes smaller, due to an increase in membrane conductance, the amplitude of the conducted impulses increase. (From Wolbarsht,[103] Fig. 13.)

result from the flow of current from entirely different ionic generators. The question now arises as to the ion species which are involved in these respective currents. Now the excitatory receptor potentials depolarize the membrane from its resting level of about −70 millivolts. This depolarization must, therefore, involve the movement of ions with an electrochemical equilibrium considerably below the resting level. It should thus be possible to abolish such ionic currents by changing their electrochemical gradient.  In the case of the generator potential of the *Limulus* eccentric cell, net current flow across the membrane theoretically disappears at a membrane potential of −8 millivolts (figure 29), indicating that at this level the e.m.f. which drives the generator

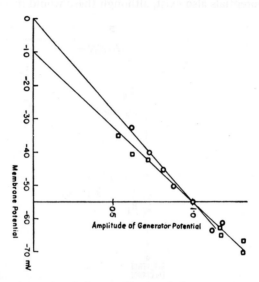

FIG. 32.  A graph of the amplitude of the generator potential (receptor potential) in a crustacean stretch receptor neuron as a function of the ambient resting membrane potential.  In the two curves shown, extrapolations indicate that the receptor potential amplitude declines to zero when the ambient membrane potential is at 0 and − 10 millivolts, respectively.  It is concluded that the equilibrium potential of the ionic current generators responsible for the receptor potential is close to these levels of membrane potential, since, net current flowing across the membrane is very small or absent altogether.  (From Terzuolo and Washizu,[96] Fig. 4.)

currents has been effectively removed.  Similar results were obtained in the crustacean stretch-receptor cell (fig. 32), where the equilibrium level for the receptor potential is close to zero. The extracellular ion most likely to be implicated in the generation of the receptor potential would in fact seem to be sodium, since it is highly concentrated in the extracellular environment and, under certain conditions, is known to pass selectively across the membrane and depolarize it. However, the equilibrium potential of this ion is about $+45$ millivolts in most preparations, and this is a much greater level of depolarization (actually a reversal of membrane polarity) than those quoted above. Presumably, therefore, some other ion species must also move with sodium and limit its influence upon the membrane potential. It has been suggested that an outward movement of potassium ions would be consistent with these findings, and in fact experiments with synaptic structures indicate that excitatory potentials produced following release of chemical transmitter from a presynaptic neuron do involve potassium ions.[22] Experiments with sensory structures have been confined to observations on the effects following the removal of sodium ions from the extracellular medium. Following such treatment, the amplitude of the receptor potential obtained from a standard stimulus in the Pacinian corpuscle has been found to undergo a reduction by up to 90 per cent.[20, 39] There still remains a residual depolarization, however, which is not reversibly dependent upon the presence of sodium ions (fig. 33). Similar results to these were obtained following application of sodium-free solution to the frog muscle spindle.[17, 59, 86] In these experiments, the receptor potential was reduced, within several minutes, by 70 to 80 per cent., but was never completely abolished in a reversible manner. It may therefore be concluded that, while sodium ions are certainly involved in the ionic current responsible for generating the receptor potential, other ion species also take part. Moreover, these must be in addition to the suspected involvement of potassium ions. This supposition is based on the fact that while the potassium equilibrium potential is presumably at a greater membrane potential than occurs at rest, the residual receptor potential remaining after removal of sodium from the external medium is still depolarizing in direction. In the report mentioned above,[17] CALMA found that reduction of the normal calcium ion concentration was effective in reducing the size of the receptor potential, and indeed it has now been shown that calcium can take part in the inward excitatory current in several different excitable tissues.[44, 64] In CALMA's experiments, however, these effects were countered by raising the magnesium ion content of the medium, and in view of the antagonistic effects of these two ions with respect to the excitability of nerve cell membranes, it would be pointless to suggest that these results can be explained purely on the basis of removal and replacement of part of the receptor membrane e.m.f.

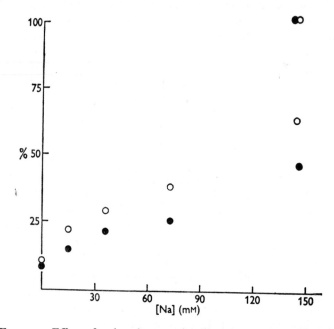

FIG. 33.   Effect of reduced external sodium ion concentration on the amplitude of the receptor potential in the Pacinian corpuscle. Abscissa: external sodium concentration.   Ordinate, amplitude of the receptor potential (open circles) or its rate of rise (closed circles) expressed as per cent of the value obtained to an identical stimulus in normal Ringer solution. (From Diamond et al.,[20] Fig. 8.)

Certain species of fish, notably from the families Gymnotidae and Mormyridae, are well known for their ability to produce fields of electrical potential in the surrounding water.[68]   Many of these animals generate such weak fields that there is little ground for supposing that they take any direct part in offensive or defensive activities of the animal.   There is, however, a large body of experimental evidence which indicates that the fish can use the electric fields—or rather the distortions which occur in these fields—to locate objects in the surrounding water.[28, 45, 46, 67, 99]

BENNETT has examined some sensory cells in Mormyrids which appear to be implicated in the detection of potential field variations. Briefly, he has found three types of cells, all of which are sensitive to potential differences orientated along the transverse axis of the animal. In all cases the receptor cells make functional contact with second-order neurons at the periphery. It was of especial interest to examine their mode of excitation, because at first glance they would appear to violate the doctrine of electrical inexcitability of the receptor cell membrane enunciated in Chapter 2. From the results of his experiments, however, BENNETT suggests two types of sensory mechanisms which do not involve changes in the resistance of the external (receptive) face of the cells involved. In one type, very small potential gradients are envisaged, which directly cause the release of a chemical transmitter at the peripheral synapse by the sensory cell. With such a mechanism, the external face of the cell is presumed to act purely as a resistive element to inward current-flow generated by the potential gradients in the external medium, as exemplified by the ampullary receptors of figure 34. The resultant depolarization of the sensory cell would thus directly effect the release of transmitter substance from its internal face, just as in the nerve terminations in a presynaptic neuron.[22] The other type of sensory mechanism postulated is conceptually more complex. The theory of its operation is exemplified by the tuberous receptor and is shown in figure 34. According to this hypothesis, the external face of the receptor cell consists of a membrane with extremely high electrical resistance and a large capacitance. Thus, current flow can occur through this membrane only when there are changes in the external field strength, i.e. during charging or discharging of the large capacitance associated with the external face of the cell. The membrane comprising the inner (synaptic) face of the cell is supposed to be electrically excitable in the classical sense, so that with sufficient depolarization by an inward capacitative current at the external face of the cell, regenerative activity occurs at the inner face and is transmitted to second-order neurons through either chemical or electrical synaptic structures. BENNETT's hypothetical capacitative mechanisms is intriguing and revives an idea originally introduced by KATZ[59] to explain the phenomenon of the receptor potential generated by mechanical deformation of the muscle spindle. However, whilst recognizing its plausibility, KATZ dismissed his proposal on quantitative grounds. The hypothesis put forward by BENNETT has so far held up under the scrutiny of various experimental procedures.

### Tonic, Ampullary Receptor

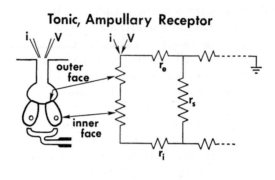

### Phasic, Tuberous Receptor

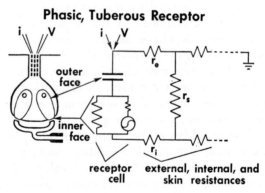

FIG. 34.    Diagrams of the anatomy of two types of electroreceptors found in Mormyrids and their electrical analogs.  Ampullary, or tonic, receptors act as series resistances to current flowing as the result of an impressed voltage.  Outward current across the inner face of the receptor cells presumably liberates a chemical transmitter and excites second-order sensory nerve fibers.  The tuberous, or phasic, type of receptors have a large membrane capacitance associated with their outer face; thus, even small changes in voltage of the external medium result in large current fluxes across the membrane of the inner face of the cell.  When this current is directed outward, it triggers an action potential across the membrane and a transmitter substance is liberated.  (Courtesy of M. V. L. Bennett.)

## Summary

The immediate effect of most types of stimulus energy is to cause an increase in the conductance of the membrane of the receptor cell or primary sensory neuron to which it has functional access. The result of such a change in the membrane characteristics is a flow of ionic current which can alter the polarity of the cell. In the case of depolarizing receptor currents, both sodium and potassium ions are probably involved, as well as other unspecified ion species. If the current is of sufficient intensity, adjacent regions of the cell will be depolarized to levels below threshold, and nerve impulses will be generated. Receptor potentials may conceivably be generated by mechanisms other than increases in membrane conductance; so far there is only evidence for their operation in some fish sensory cells which have been implicated in the detection of variations of weak external electric fields.

# 5 : Sensory Cell Function and Architecture

A good many problems concerning the relationship between form and function which are common to all neurons may be more conveniently examined in sensory neurons in particular. For example, the nature of the processes involved in impulse initiation in primary sensory neurons presents problems which differ in each cellular morphology and, often, in each neuron population. In particular, a consideration of neuron geometry is critical in terms of logistics as well as the limiting physical properties of the membrane. For example, crustacean stretch receptor neurons have distributed loci which serve a transducer function. These loci are, in fact, the terminations of the numerous dendritic arborizations which are imbedded in the central region of the muscle receptor organs. It is not inconceivable that impulses initiated in one dendrite (by stretch applied to the receptor muscle) might propagate into adjacent dendritic branches, as well as orthodromically toward the central nervous system. Retrograde firing in this fashion would block by collision any impulse activity set up in adjacent branches. One can foresee that, if firing frequency in adjacent branches were unequal, the characteristic frequency from the branch that generated the most impulses per unit time would invariably dominate the output of the cell as a whole. If it happened that stimulus energy were coupled to different dendritic branches in an unequal fashion, equal increments in stimulus energy would surely not be detected as such by the different dendritic branches, and one might conceivably even find a situation where stimulus strength had increased, but the output frequency of the cell had actually decreased. Thus, there are distinct advantages in having the location of impulse initiation on the final common pathway of information flow, i.e. the axon. Difficulties encountered by the interaction of separate regions initiating regenerative activity are thereby avoided, and the soma and dendritic tree form an integrative unit which summates graded, electrical activity from all available transducer loci.

In all cases in which the question has been examined, the region of membrane in a primary sensory neuron which is concerned with the transduction of stimulus energy to graded electrical activity appears to be electrically inexcitable, and spike initiation occurs at a more proximal location along the neuron. In the crayfish slowly-adapting stretch-neuron, the finer dendritic branches (i.e. those imbedded in the receptor muscle and exposed to mechanical deformation) apparently do not support impulse activity[27] and spike initiation occurs on the axon proper, at a point several hundred microns central to the cell body. The data illustrated in figure 35 provide unambiguous evidence that spikes arise first at a point central to the soma. Now the extracellular records of the electrical changes surrounding an axon immersed in a volume conductor (saline) show the approaching impulse at the active electrode first as a positive-going potential change relative to a distant point in the medium; for action currents just ahead of the spike cross the membrane in an outward direction. As the impulse itself passes underneath the electrode the current-flux is inward (negative-going) but again becomes outwardly-directed as the spike passes by. Thus, the sequence ' source-sink-source ' can be detected only when an impulse is actively propagated past an external recording point on the cell. An impulse which approaches, but never actually reaches, the region of membrane beneath the recording electrode will be detected only as a positive deflexion; while an electrode at the site of origin of the spike will record a negative potential followed by a positive one. These concepts can be related to the records in figure 35. At some point on the axon, the configuration of the action potential generated by an adequate stimulus to the receptor was found to be a diphasic one (with negative-positive phases) in contrast to the triphasic waveform obtained at all other loci. Presumably, impulses are initiated at one point on the axon and then propagate peripherally towards the soma as well as towards the central nervous system.  The sequential advance of the action potential recorded at loci between this point and the soma was found to be consistent with this view.

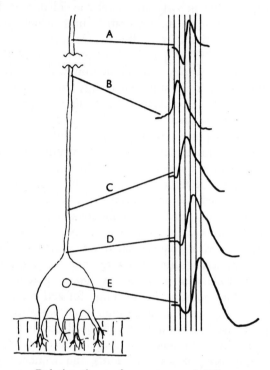

FIG. 35.    Relative times of occurrence of different parts of the action potential wave-form as recorded extracellularly from different regions of a crayfish stretch receptor neuron. The impulse appears first as a diphasic transient at B, a point about 500 microns central to the cell body.  (From Edwards and Ottoson,[23] Fig. 1.)

Investigations of multichanneled central neurons in a variety of preparations have resulted in essentially similar findings.  The soma and dendritic regions of the cell are intimately involved in the generation of graded, non-regenerative potential changes under the influence of synaptic transmitter substances, and they may even be secondarily invaded by antidromically propagating impulses. These latter impulses, however, are initiated first in the membrane of the axon or axon hillock region, not in the soma-dendrite complex.[95]

Even if the axonal membrane is not more responsive to generator currents than other parts of the cell, the above results may be predicted from neuron geometry. Depolarizing currents (flowing within the cell from a source region on the dendritic tree) will cross the membrane in an outward direction, both in the soma and the initial reaches of the axon. The small diameter of the axon, compared with that of the cell body, means that the density of outward current may be greater in the former region, even though most of the total available current will be drawn by the relatively great capacitance of the soma membrane. In addition, there is now some evidence[95] that the excitability of the axon membrane may, in fact, be inherently greater than that of the soma. Thus, the initial activation of the impulse at an axonal locus appears to be certain.

The most ubiquitous type of primary sensory neuron is of the simple bipolar configuration. The somata of these cells are usually located at the periphery of an animal and are often quite close to the region of stimulus transduction. None the less, the thin distal processes of such cells may be several hundred microns in length. Considering the expected decrement in amplitude of a receptor potential generated at the tip, it is not surprising to find that impulse-initiation can occur at a locus which is distal to the cell body. Evidence for this statement comes from a preparation in which the sensory neurons in question are large enough to be examined with intracellular electrodes. The cells in question occur in pairs within the hypodermis of the crayfish carapace. These cells possess a directional sensitivity, and they are activated to different extents depending upon the direction in which the structural parts of the receptor organs are moved by the stimulus.[77] The external structural part of each receptor is a thin hair, or sensillum; it can be moved by the flow of water past the parent animal, and depending upon whether the direction of flow is anteriorly or posteriorly directed, one or the other neuron from each pair will respond. In the region of the thoracic carapace the hypodermis exists as a thin sheet of tissue. The somata of the sensory neurons are some 50 – 80 microns long, and under favorable conditions, they can be visualized in living preparations. An electrode can, thus, be inserted into the soma of one of these neurons. Such an intracellular electrode rarely records a pre-potential to an impulse or anything resembling a receptor potential in response to mechanical stimulation of the receptor organ—only propagating impulses are seen. However, the waveform of the latter is strictly dependent upon the direction of approach to the cell body. Antidromically-propagated impulses are invariably inflected on the rising phase of the transient, probably due to a slight delay in conduction at the axon-soma boundary. On the other hand, orthodromic impulses from healthy preparations are rarely inflected, and the rate of potential change on the rising phase of the spike undergoes no obvious variations until it peaks out. These observations lead one to the conclusion that impulses must not originate at an axonal locus (i.e. proximal to the cell body); for, if a receptor potential of sufficient amplitude ($2 - 10$ mV) to generate impulses had spread to the axon, logically it should have been detected by an electrode in the soma—a region of the cell much closer to the transducer locus, and thus to the source of the receptor currents. Secondly, impulses known to be invading the soma from an axonal (antidromic) direction are always inflected, whereas impulses evoked by natural stimuli are usually uninflected, and must therefore be entering the soma over another path-way. In some instances, cells were injured by the micro-electrode and the character of the response to stimuli deteriorated during the course of an experiment. Initially, this took the form of a marked inflection appearing on the rising phase of ortho-dromic, as well as antidromic, impulses. The amplitude of the inflected region of the spike was, however, invariably different in the two cases. Characteristically different impulse configurations were thus observable during invasion of the soma by, respectively, orthodromic and antidromic spikes.

Further support for the concept that the initiation of ortho-dromic impulses occurs at a locus distal to the soma was obtained following electrical stimulation of the distal process and mechanical stimulation of the receptor organ. The results of these experi-ments are shown in figure 36: in it four superimposed traces indicate the variable waveform of impulses recorded from the soma of an injured cell, following mechanical stimulation of the receptor. Invasion of the soma by the spikes occurred in all instances, except one in which, perhaps due to refractoriness of the excitable membrane, only the electiotronic potential from a distantly-blocked impulse was seen. After these records had been

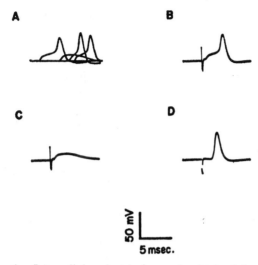

FIG. 36. Intracellular electrical records obtained from the soma of a crustacean bipolar mechanosensory neuron. The cell was in an unhealthy condition, and orthodromic impulses initiated by mechanical stimuli (A) had rather unusual waveforms, indicating a delayed invasion of the soma (and in one case, non-invasion) by the centrally propagating impulses. Similar waveforms were obtained following electrical stimulation of the distal process of the cell (B), (C). The record in D is of an antidromic impulse. (From Mellon and Kennedy,[79] Fig. 7.)

photographed, several brief electrical shocks were delivered to the distal process. These stimuli initiated impulses which propagated towards the soma. The responses obtained in two of these instances can be seen in figure 36 B and C. The waveforms of the two closely resemble those obtained following mechanical stimulation and are quite unlike that of an invading antidromic impulse (figure 36D). The results strongly support the concept of a distal locus for the site of initiation of propagated impulses in these cells. Quite recently, results similar to these have been obtained in different cells—the proprioceptor bipolar sensory neurons in the leg of a crab.[80, 81] In that preparation, injured neurons were not used for evidence, but impulses were blocked from the soma by artificially hyperpolarizing the latter. The amounts of polarization required to block orthodromic and anti-dromic spikes were found to be different, suggesting that these impulses enter the soma through different pathways. It was further shown that orthodromic spikes blocked in this manner were not recorded by an electrode placed more centrally on the axon, even though an electrotonic potential from the spike could still be recorded in the soma in response to mechanical stimulation.

Because of its large capacitance, any area of expanded membrane can be expected to draw current from adjacent regions, thereby creating a zone which has a lowered safety factor for the trans-mission of impulses. Thus, the inclusion of the soma in the conduction pathway of a neuron is likely to limit its frequency capabilities. In fact, it was found that orthodromic impulses in the crayfish thoracic sensory neurons were unable to invade the soma at frequencies higher than 200 per second. While this probably does not represent a physiological encumbrance to a crustacean, vertebrate nervous systems often depend upon afferent input frequencies of 1000 per second. This may be the reason why, in this group, many somatic afferents are monopolar structures having their cell bodies to one side of the major conducting path.

The initiation of impulses in vertebrate mechanoreceptors, such as the Pacinian corpuscle, appears to be comparable to the situation described above for the bipolar neuron. In the Pacinian corpuscle, the distal tip of the nerve fiber is a mechano-electrical transducer, and a receptor current flows when its membrane is compressed. The axon of this cell is myelinated, and it is inter-esting to note that the myelin sheath extends well out towards the tip of the fiber and may even overlie regions (fig. 37) which are electrically-inexcitable, for impulses are initiated more centrally, at the first node of Ranvier. It would be interesting to confirm this suggestion, for it may represent a true channeling of receptor current by an extracellular structure, the myelin sheath. Another preparation in which this principle may operate is the mechanosensory neuron studied by WOLBARSHT.[103] The region of this cell which separates the tip of the distal process from the impulse-initiating region (at or near the cell body) runs through an extracellular channel which has an extremely high electrical resistance. The current which enters the cell at the transducer locus near the tip of the distal process may consequently attain high outward density in the region of the cell body, where the spikes are probably generated.[104, 105]

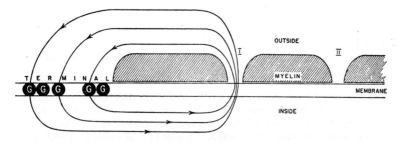

FIG. 37.   Diagram of the membrane and myelin sheath in the region of the nerve terminal in a Pacinian corpuscle.   I, II indicate, respectively, the first and second nodes of Ranvier.  The elements labeled G represent separate independent generators of current on the electrically-inexcitable membrane of the nerve terminal; hypothetical lines of current flow due to a stimulus are indicated.[70]

By far the most elusive of the properties of sensory cells which influence impulse initiation are those factors affecting the functional nature of the membrane itself.   Little is known concerning the structural differences between electrically excitable and inexcitable membranes.   The final classification of a particular region into one of these categories must always depend upon electrophysiological analysis.   The resolution obtainable by these techniques is not nearly as fine as could be wished for, and no complete functional map of the membrane has yet been executed successfully for any neuron.   Some extreme examples can be cited, however, which may be susceptible to experimental analysis, a likely one being large, completely electrically-inexcitable structures, such as arthropod central somata.   Most axons, by definition, possess electrically-excitable plasma membrane, but even this property is, in the strictest sense, a generic term embracing various types of response to identical electrical stimuli.   This point is clearly illustrated in figure 38.  As mentioned above, the axon, soma, and some of the distal process of the bipolar thoracic sensory neurons in the crayfish are electrically excitable and

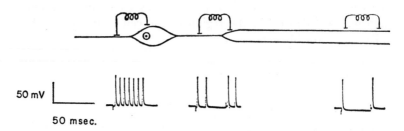

50 mV

50 msec.

FIG. 38.    Results of an experiment illustrating the differential responsiveness of neighboring regions on a sensory neuron.  An intracellular recording electrode was within the expanded region of the axon, well central to the location of the soma.  A pair of extracellular stimulating electrodes was moved along the neuron, and stimuli were given at several locations, three of which are shown in the diagram.  When the electrode pair was in the region of the soma-dendrite boundary, a 35-msec. current pulse elicited a train of seven impulses.  At two regions on the axon central to the soma, identical stimuli evoked, respectively, two and one impulses each, at the onset and cessation of the current pulse.  (From Mellon and Kennedy,[79] Fig. 10.)

support impulse propagation.  The response of this electrically-excitable membrane to prolonged electric currents can be quantitatively different from one region of the cell to the next, however.  Thus, while many impulses may be generated when the current is applied to the distal process, only one arises when the stimulating current is confined to the axon region.  On the other hand, axons of central neurons in arthropods have been shown to receive synaptic contacts from other nerve cells, so that both electrically-excitable and inexcitable regions must exist in close proximity and may even form a functional mosaic.  Electrophysiological techniques with much greater resolution than now exists will be needed to provide accurate functional maps of neural membranes.  The development of such refined techniques may make it possible to recognize correlations between various physiological properties of the membrane and its fine structure.

## Summary

The impulse-initiating regions of a sensory neuron are determined both by gross neuron geometry and by functional divisions within the membrane of the cell. The transducer locus of a cell must be connected to those regions where impulse initiation occurs by a low resistance pathway, for sufficient current must pass outward across the membrane of the latter regions to depolarize the membrane to threshold values. Large areas of expanded membrane, such as neuron somata, tend to draw current by their large capacitances; this process may deprive adjacent axonal regions of sufficient current to trigger conducted impulses. Usually, however, membrane in the axon hillock region of various nerve cells is modified (by as yet unknown parameters) so that it has a greater excitability to outward currents than other parts of the cell; such areas of low-threshold membrane normally constitute the site of initiation of orthodromic impulses.

# 6 : Absorption of Stimulus Energy

While the molecular architecture of the receptor membrane and the alterations which occur during application of a stimulus remain very largely unknown, some inferences can be made concerning structural organization from the nature of electrical changes evoked by increments in stimulus energy. Thus, it has become convenient to regard sensory membranes as containing a multiplicity of independent sites. Each of these sites is supposed to be capable of absorbing a fixed amount of stimulus energy, and all of them must be activated before the maximal response of a sensory cell (or sensory neuron) can be realized. According to this hypothesis, each site converts part of the stimulus into a receptor current, larger receptor potentials being obtained by the recruitment of additional current generators. It follows from this idea that the progressive removal of small amounts of the receptor membrane should have little effect upon the receptor potential, other than a reduction in its amplitude in proportion to the percentage of sites lost. An experiment designed to examine this premise was successfully carried out with the Pacinian corpuscle.[71] The receptor membrane of this sensory neuron consists of an encapsulated (but non-myelinated) nerve-ending. If the capsule is carefully removed, the nerve-ending may be stimulated directly with a fine probe (as illustrated by the records in figure 39). Single, identical mechanical stimuli applied to the nerve-ending resulted in progressively smaller receptor potentials as increasing fractions of the total membrane were removed. However, neither the response latency nor the waveform was interfered with. The implications of these results were clearly stated by the authors: ' No matter where the cut or compression was done, or how many were made, the intact remains of non-myelinated terminal in connection with the myelinated axon were always capable of giving detectable generator potentials upon mechanical stimulation. This suggests that the generator potential arises at membrane parts which are able to function independently of each other; and that these parts are scattered all over the non-myelinated nerve-ending.'

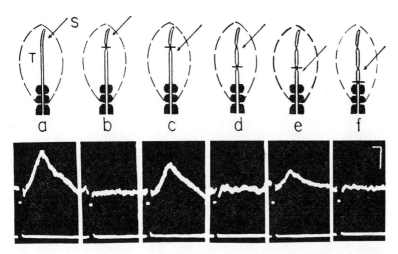

FIG. 39.    Records illustrating the independent nature of different regions of the receptive membrane in a Pacinian corpuscle.    The integrity of the entire nerve-ending is not necessary for a receptor potential to be evoked; destruction (b–e) of varying amounts of receptive membrane abolishes only proportional percentages of receptor potential amplitude.    Arrows indicate regions of application of the mechanical stimulus in each case. (From Loewenstein and Rathkamp.[71])

The concept of independent multiple receptor sites has also been applied to the chemoreceptor membrane and is implicit in a theoretical treatment of this phenomenon developed by BEIDLER[12] in 1954.    In attempting to explain some data obtained from mammalian taste cells, BEIDLER assumed that these cells, like proteins, bind salts at specific loci on their membrane structure. He further assumed that the binding reaction obeys the mass law, and that, being in thermodynamic equilibrium, it is independent of time.    From these assumptions, the reaction of a

S.O.—G

stimulating substance with the free receptor sites on the membrane can be written as follows:

$$C + (S\text{-}N) \rightleftharpoons N \tag{1}$$

and

$$KC = N/(S\text{-}N), \tag{2}$$

where $N$ is the number of sites occupied by the stimulus at any concentration, $C$, $S$ is the total number of sites available, and $K$ is the equilibrium constant of the reaction.  Neither $S$ nor $N$ was known to BEIDLER, but by making the further assumption that the maximum response of the sense organ, $R_m$, and the response at any lower concentration of stimulus, $R$, are directly proportional to, respectively, the unknown values for total number and for occupied sites, these experimentally determined parameters may be appropriately substituted in the above equation which, rearranged, gives the following relationship:

$$C/R = C/R_m + 1/KR_m. \tag{3}$$

If none of the assumptions in the theory is violated by the reaction of the sense cell with a stimulating substance, a plot of $C/R$ vs. $C$ should yield a straight line whose slope is equal to $1/R_m$. Measurements made by BEIDLER, using data from mammalian taste buds, fulfilled this criterion.  The theory may also be applicable to single salt sensitive primary sensory neurons in the blowfly, *Phormia*.[26]  Data from these cells are, for technical reasons, easier to interpret than those obtained from second-order neurons in the mammalian chorda tympanic nerve (the preparation used by BEIDLER).  Since the salt-sensitive neurons of the blowfly are rather insensitive, fairly high concentrations (up to six molal) of stimulating salt were used.  To obviate any errors due to solute self-interaction in these experiments, the effective concentration (i.e. the mean thermodynamic activity) of the salt was calculated and the numerical values $(\bar{a}_{\pm})$ used in plotting the graphs of equation (3).  The result of one such plot is shown in figure 40.  The curve is satisfactorily linear, the slope being identical with the measured value for the maximum response of the sensory neuron.  Thus there seems to be sufficient evidence for tentatively accepting BEIDLER'S ion-binding theory as a reasonable representation of the observed reaction between stimulating salts and the sensory membrane. Some objections can be made to it. For example, most of the early experimental work with *Phormia* gave little indication that the anion of a salt was of any importance in determining response magnitude; however, this conclusion may not be strictly correct.[35] In addition, values for the equilibrium constant, calculated from

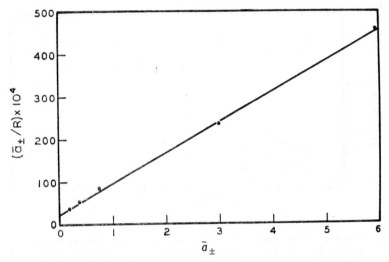

FIG. 40. A plot of the equation, $a/R = a/R_m + 1/R_m K$, using data obtained from the response of a blowfly chemosensory neuron to different concentrations of sodium chloride. (From Evans and Mellon,[26] Fig. 3.)

data obtained from the *Phormia* sense organs, were found to vary over a considerable range. This finding casts doubt upon the assumption that the reaction of a stimulating substance with the membrane is in a true state of thermodynamic equilibrium. The objection might be overcome if it could be shown that the reaction is in a steady-state condition, but further evidence will be necessary before this can be resolved.

One curious finding with the blowfly salt receptor has been that potassium and sodium salts are about equally effective in eliciting a response from the sensory neuron. Even neglecting the slight contribution of the anion to the response, one finds the maximum response to highly-concentrated solutions of both salts

S.O.—G*

is identical (fig. 41). The contact chemoreceptors of *Phormia* and many other insects are found in hair-like sensilla-tricoidea which are perforated at their tip. The dendrites of one or more chemosensory neurons run within the shank of these sensilla to the openings at the tip (fig. 42). It is presumed that stimulating substances make contact with the primary sense cells at the tip.

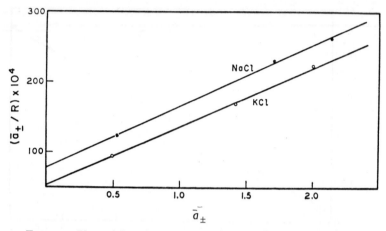

FIG. 41.    Plots of the adsorption equation using data from a blowfly neuron in response to potassium chloride and sodium chloride solutions. Note that the slopes of the two curves are very similar. (From Evans and Mellon,[26] Fig. 5.)

Now the composition of the extracellular fluid within the hair canal is unknown; however, since impulses can propagate for some distance out along the distal process,[105] there is good reason to suppose that the concentration of extracellular sodium is close to normal. If this is so, it is a puzzling fact that sodium ions themselves appear to constitute an adequate stimulus for the neurons, for the latter are known to remain electrically silent unless an externally applied solution of this ion (or other stimulating substance) comes in contact with the tip of the sensillum. Now, the stimulating effects of concentrated potassium solutions would not be hard to understand, in view of the depolarization caused by high extracellular concentrations of this ion species in other nervous tissues. At high concentrations, however, potassium is no more effective than—indeed, is identical to—sodium in this

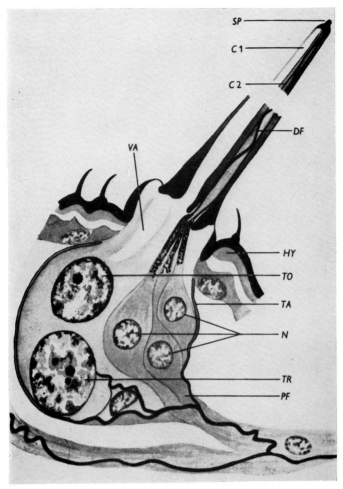

FIG. 42. An illustration showing the morphology of the cellular elements associated with a blowfly trichoid sensillum. Not all the nervous elements known to be present in such structures have been included in the drawing. $C_1$, thin-walled hair canal; $C_2$ thick-walled hair canal, within which course the distal fibers ($DF$) of the sensory neurons ($N$); $HY$, hypodermis; $TR$, $TO$, trichogen and tormogen cells, respectively. $PF$: proximal nerve fiber; $SP$: sensory pore. (After Dethier,[19] Fig. 2.)

respect. It is possible, of course, that the dendrite tip is bathed in a medium which is unlike the normal extracellular fluid, or, alternatively, that the properties of the dendritic membrane are unique with regard to their permeability characteristics.    In either case, the fact that absorption of a stimulating substance had occurred would have to be transmitted to the more conventional impulse-supporting membrane regions of the dendrite.    Any modifications in the permeability properties, as suggested above, would also require rather unconventional mechanisms for the generation of receptor currents, and these have yet to be proposed, or even seriously considered.

Experiments performed in recent years by HAGINS and his colleagues[42, 43] upon primary photoreceptor cells of the squid have amply demonstrated that multiple independent sites for the absorption and transduction of stimulus energy occur in these structures.    To do this, extracellular electrodes were positioned at different depths within a slice of squid retina, so as to record potentials at different points along the rather long outer segments of the primary visual cells.    The experimental situation and some results can be seen in figure 43.    In the unexcited state, there was no potential difference between the electrodes, A and B, since both were extracellular, and $V_B - V_A = 0$.    Now, a stimulating light would be expected to produce an inward current (i.e. a current sink) in the receptor cell membrane.    This does, in fact, happen, but the locus of this sink is strictly confined to the region of the sense organ upon which the light impinges, no matter how bright it is, and this locus moves when the stimulus moves.    In the diagram shown in figure 43, the stimulus spot at A produces a maximum current sink at this electrode, so that $V_B - V_A$ approaches large positive values.    As the spot is moved towards B, the current sink passes through a region equidistant between the two electrodes (i.e. the external resistances between the spot and the two electrodes are roughly equal) and the potential between them falls to zero.    As the spot is moved past this point, the sign of the potential reverses, and at B, maximum negative values for $V_B - V_A$ are recorded.    Under normal conditions of stimulation, the entire outer segment of each sensory cell would be exposed to the incident light, so that the current sink would encompass its whole length.    The bulk of the outward current then apparently emerges from the region of the cell body, which is screened from the incident light energy by a layer of pigment cells (the region labeled P in figure 43). Experiments with a confined light source simply demonstrate that the influence of the stimulus is strictly localized to the directly affected areas of membrane. These areas can apparently respond independently of surrounding unexcited regions. These conclusions, concerning the relation between response magnitude and per cent. of sensory

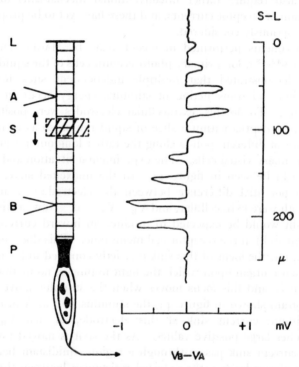

FIG. 43.    Diagram of a single photoreceptor cell of a squid, and the results of potential measurements along the outer segment of the cell due to passage of a light stimulus along it. Each sub-unit of the cell membrane responds to light independently of the rest of the cell—a current sink occurs only in that region which is being illuminated by the stimulus. *Abscissa*: Voltage difference between the fixed electrodes, A and B. *Ordinate*: Position of the stimulus (S) from the outer tip of the receptor cell (L). (From Hagins, Zonana and Adams,[43] Fig. 2.)

membrane affected, are similar to those drawn for the two other examples given in this chapter.   It also follows that a maximum response would necessarily include all available sites of the membrane where photoelectric conversion can occur.

Additional evidence of the independence of adjacent stimulus sites was obtained from experiments employing selective light adaptation.   Hagins found experimentally that a region of squid photoreceptor cell which has been subjected to sufficient light to bleach 5 per cent. of its visual pigment undergoes a ten-fold increase in photic threshold (as measured by the size of the receptor potential).   However, adjacent regions of the cell which has been partially light-adapted in this manner were found to have retained their control values of sensitivity.   Thus, whatever steps are involved in the conversion of photic energy into increases in membrane conductance, each part of the membrane appears to be able to effect them independently of the rest.   There is, in fact, no interference between adjacent parts by chemical products or alterations of membrane structure.

A critical question which remains concerns the precise mechanisms by which the breakdown of pigment in a photoreceptor cell is coupled to changes in the electrical properties of the membrane.   Perhaps the most plausible hypothesis is that a chemical released by the photolytic reaction diffuses to nearby membrane regions and there induces the standard increases in ionic conductance.[42]   According to this interpretation photoreceptors are one type of chemoreceptor, with the provision that the adequate stimulus not only affects the membrane from the inside surface, but is endogenously produced !   ARVANITAKI and CHALAZONITIS have recently shown[7] that certain dyes injected into living axons can couple light energy to the cell membrane, and depolarization and spiking occur throughout the period of illumination.   Perhaps a more intensive research with model photoreceptor systems like this will lead to a greater understanding of those which have evolved their own specific pigment complement.

Very little more can be said at present about the actual physical changes in the sensory membrane which result from energy absorption.   There can be no doubt that some of the remaining problems in sensory physiology, such as the control of impulse frequency by membrane potential, will eventually yield to electro-physiological analysis.  But it is becoming increasingly clear that these techniques, at least at their present level of sophistication, will not be adequate for meaningful analyses of the primary structural or configurational changes which the stimulus imparts to the sensory cell.  Models, using convenient living preparations,

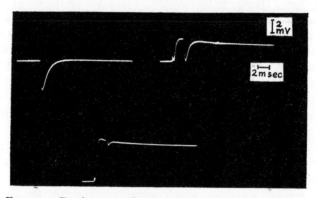

FIG. 44.    Conductance change in the membrane of a lobster axon due to a mechanical stimulus.    A brief current pulse (top, left) is reduced in amplitude when it is superimposed upon a ' receptor potential ' evoked from the axon membrane by a direct mechanical stimulus.    Effects of two different stimulus-strengths are shown.    (From Goldman.[36])

can be useful.    GOLDMAN[36] has found that isolated giant axons of the lobster respond to mechanical forces which tend to stretch the axonal membrane.    A large increase in membrane conductance occurs which can depolarize the axon sufficiently to fire an impulse (fig. 44).    GOLDMAN suggests that this occurs as a specific result of stretching, which would be expected to increase the distance between molecular elements of the membrane.    However, this suggestion remains in the realm of conjecture, for we have little knowledge about the mechanics of membrane changes.    Nothing has been said so far of the work being carried out on the sensory responses of higher plants, such as those found in the Venus fly-trap.[55]    Receptor potentials can be recorded from these organisms, and they may prove to be more favorable experimental material than animal preparations for an analysis of the primary effects of energy absorption. However, electrophysiological studies with these preparations have only just started.

Interesting work is now being done on the properties of artificial membranes and the behavior of monomolecular films, and it may very well be that this field of physical chemistry will provide the questions—if not the answers—upon which to base intelligent biophysical experimentation. For example, the membrane alterations which account for an increased ionic conductance are undoubtedly accompanied by shifts in molecular spacing, and these may be diagnostically related to changes in intermolecular bond strength (as measurable by alterations in tensile or compressional strength of an axon), the ability of a membrane protein to scatter light, or the absorption of incident light at a specific wavelength. In view of the success which other physical techniques, such as X-ray diffraction analysis, have brought to the study of biological structure, these thoughts seem to be not unduly optimistic.

## Summary

We are only just beginning to inquire into the primary structural changes which occur subsequent to the absorption of stimulus energy at receptors. We may now state that the receptor membrane appears to consist of multiple independent sites, all of which contribute a small part to the overall electrical response effected by the stimulus. However, we have very little idea of the molecular definition of the changes which result in the response. Electrophysiological techniques will probably be insufficient for the task of advancing this aspect of research on receptor mechanisms; and the advent of other physical approaches, having considerably more resolution on the molecular scale of events, seems inevitable.

# Acknowledgements

My thanks for the use of copyright illustrations are due to authors and editors of works and periodicals mentioned in the legends and in the References, and to the following proprietors and publishers:

Academic Press Inc., New York; American Association for the Advancement of Science, Washington, D.C.; American Institute of Biological Sciences, Washington, D.C.; American Physiological Society, Bethesda, Md.; American Scientist, Princeton, New Jersey; Chatto & Windus, Ltd., London; The Journal of Physiology, Cambridge (England); Long Island Biological Association, Long Island, New York; Macmillan (Journals) Ltd., London; Pergamon Press Ltd., Oxford; Quarterly Review of Biology, State University of New York; The Rockefeller University Press, New York; The Royal Society, London; W. B. Saunders Company, Philadelphia, Pa.; The Wistar Institute of Anatomy and Biology, Philadelphia, Pa.

Grateful thanks are due to Dr H. W. Lissman for reading the manuscript and offering invaluable advice and critical comments. I would especially like to thank Dr J. E. Treherne for his many helpful suggestions on the manuscript. Much of the book was written while I was a visitor in the Zoological Laboratory, University of Cambridge, and I thank both the staff of the laboratory, who helped in reproducing the illustrations, and the John Simon Guggenheim Memorial Foundation, whose generous financial support made my visit possible.

# References

1. ADRIAN, E. D. 1926. The impulses produced by sensory nerve endings. *J. Physiol*, **61**: 49.
2. —— 1928. *The Basis of Sensation*. Christophers, London.
3. —— 1932. *The Mechanism of Nervous Action*. Oxford University Press.
4. ADRIAN, E. D. and ZOTTERMAN, Y. 1926. Impulses from a single sensory end-organ. *J. Physiol.*, **61**: viii.
5. ALEXANDROWICZ, J. S. 1951. Muscle receptor organs in the abdomen of *Homarus vulgaris* and *Palinurus vulgaris*. *Quart. J. Micr. Sci.*, **92**: 163.
6. ALVAREZ-BUYLLA, R. and RAMIREZ DE ARELLANO, J. 1953. Local responses in Pacinian corpuscles. *Am. J. Physiol.*, **172**: 237.
7. ARVANITAKI, A. and CHALAZONITIS, N. 1961. Excitatory and inhibitory processes initiated by light and infra-red radiation in single identifiable nerve cells. In: *Nervous Inhibition* (Ed. E. Florey). Pergamon Press, Oxford.
8. AUTRUM, H. 1959. Non photic receptors in lower forms. In: *Handbook of Physiology. I. Neurophysiology.* American Physiological Society, Washington, D.C.
9. BARRON, D. H. and MATTHEWS, B. H. C. 1938. The interpretation of potential changes in the spinal cord. *J. Physiol.*, **92**: 276.
10. BARTH, J. 1964. Intracellular recording from photoreceptor neurons in the eyes of a nudibranch mollusc (*Hermissenda crassicornis*). *Comp. Biochem. Physiol.*, **11**: 311.
11. BEHRENS, M. E. and WULFF, V. J. 1965. Light-initiated responses of retinula and eccentric cells in the *Limulus* lateral eye. *J. gen. Physiol.*, **48**: 1081.
12. BEIDLER, L. M. 1954. A theory of taste stimulation. *J. gen. Physiol.*, **38**: 133.
13. BENNETT, M. V. L. 1965. Electroreceptors in Mormyrids. *Cold Spring Harb. Symp. quant. Biol.*, **30**: 245.
14. BENOLKEN, R. M. 1965. Regenerative transducing properties of a graded visual response. In: 'Sensory Recptors.' *Cold Spring Harb. Symp. quant. Biol.*, **30**, 445.
15. BERNHARD, C. G. and GRANIT, R. 1946. Nerve as model temperature end organ. *J. gen. Physiol.*, **29**: 257.
16. BERNHARD, C. G., GRANIT, R. and SKOGLAND, C. R. 1942. The breakdown of accommodation-nerve as a model sense organ. *J. Neurophysiol.*, **5**: 55.
17. CALMA, I. 1965. Ions and the receptor potential in the muscle spindle of the frog. *J. Physiol.*, **177**: 31.

18. DAVIS, H. 1961. Some principles of sensory receptor action. *Physiol. Rev.*, **41**: 391.

19. DETHIER, V. G. 1955. The physiology and histology of the contact chemoreceptors of the blowfly. *Quart. Rev. Biol.*, **30**: 348.

20. DIAMOND, J., GRAY, J. A. B. and INMAN, D. R. 1958. The relation between receptor potentials and the concentration of sodium ions. *J. Physiol.*, **142**: 388.

21. DOWLING, J. E. and WALD, G. 1960. The biological function of vitamin A. *Proc. Natn. Acad. Sci. U.S.A.*, **46**: 587.

22. ECCLES, J. C. 1964. *The Physiology of Synapses.* Springer-Verlag, Berlin.

23. EDWARDS, C. and OTTOSON, D. 1958. The site of impulse initiation in a nerve cell of a crustacean stretch receptor. *J. Physiol.*, **143**: 138.

24. EDWARDS, C., TERZUOLO, C. A. and WASHIZU, Y. 1963. The effect of changes of the ionic environment upon an isolated crustacean sensory neuron. *J. Neurophysiol.*, **26**: 948.

25. EVANS, D. R. and MELLON, DeF. 1962. Electrophysiological studies of a water receptor associated with the taste sensilla of the blowfly. *J. gen. Physiol.*, **45**: 487.

26. —— 1962. Stimulation of a primary taste receptor by salts. *J. gen. Physiol.*, **45**: 651.

27. EYZAGUIRRE, C. and KUFFLER, S. W. 1955. Processes of excitation in the dendrites and in the soma of single isolated sensory nerve cells of the lobster and crayfish. *J. gen. Physiol.*, **39**: 87.

28. FESSARD, A. and SZABO, T. 1961. Mise en évidence d'un récepteur sensible à l'électricité dans la peau des Mormyres. *C.R. Acad. Sci. Paris*, **253**: 1859.

29. FLOREY, E. 1957. Chemical transmission and adaptation. *J. gen. Physiol.*, **40**: 533.

30. FRÖHLICH, F. W. 1913. Beiträge zur allgemeinen Physiologie der Sinnesorgane. *Z. Sinnesphysiol.*, **48**: 28.

31. FUORTES, M. G. F. 1959. Initiation of impulses in visual cells of *Limulus*. *J. Physiol.*, **148**: 14.

32. —— 1963. Visual responses in the eye of the dragonfly. *Science*, **142**: 69.

33. FUORTES, M. G. F. and MANTEGAZZINI, F. 1962. Interpretation of repetitive firing of nerve cells. *J. gen. Physiol.*, **45**: 1163.

34. GILLARY, H. L. 1966. Stimulation of the blowfly salt receptor. I. *J. gen. Physiol.*, **50**: 337.

35. —— 1966. Stimulation of the blowfly salt receptor. III. *J. gen. Physiol.*, **50**: 359.

36. GOLDMAN, D. E. 1965. The transducer action of mechanoreceptor membranes. In: 'Sensory Receptors.' *Cold Spring Harb. Symp. quant. Biol.*, **30**: 59.

37. GRANIT, R. 1955. *Receptors and Sensory Perception.* Yale University Press, New Haven (Ct.).

38. GRAY, J. A. B. 1959. Initiation of impulses at receptors. In: *Handbook of Physiology. I. Neurophysiology.* American Physiological Society, Washington, D.C.

39. GRAY, J. A. B. and SATO, M. 1953. Properties of the receptor potential in Pacinian corpuscles. *J. Physiol.*, **122**: 610.

40. GRUNDFEST, H. 1957. Electrical inexcitability of synapses and some consequences in the central nervous system. *Physiol. Rev.*, **37**: 337.

41. —— 1965. Electrophysiology and pharmacology of different components of bioelectric transducers. *Cold Spring Harb. Symp. quant. Biol.*, **30**: 1.

42. HAGINS, W. A. 1965. Electrical signs of information flow in receptors. In: 'Sensory Recptors.' *Cold Spring Harb. Symp. quant. Biol.*, **30**: 403.

43. HAGINS, W. A., ZONANA, H. V. and ADAMS, R. G. 1962. Local membrane current in the outer segments of squid photoreceptors. *Nature*, **194**: 844.

44. HAGIWARA, S. and NAKA, K. 1964. The initiation of spike potentials in barnacle muscle fibers under low intracellular $Ca^{++}$. *J. gen. Physiol.*, **48**: 141.

45. HAGIWARA, S. and MORITA, H. 1963. Coding mechanisms of electro-receptor fibers in some electric fish. *J. Neurophysiol.*, **26**: 551.

46. HAGIWARA, S., KUSANO, K. and NEGISHI, K. 1962. Physiological properties of electroreceptors of some gymnotids. *J. Neurophysiol.*, **25**: 430.

47. HARTLINE, H. K. 1938. The discharge of impulses in the optic nerve of *Pecten* in response to illumination of the eye. *J. cell. comp. Physiol.*, **11**: 465.

48. HARTLINE, H. K. and GRAHAM, C. H. 1932. Nerve impulses from single receptors in the eye. *J. cell. comp. Physiol.*, **1**: 277.

49. HARTLINE, H. K., WAGNER, H. G. and MACNICHOL, E. F., JR. 1952. The peripheral origin of nervous activity in the visual system. *Cold Spring Harb. Symp. quant. Biol.*, **17**: 125.

50. HODGKIN, A. L. 1938. The subthreshold potentials in a crustacean nerve fiber. *Proc. R. Soc.*, ser. B, **126**: 87.

51. —— 1948. The local electric changes associated with repetitive action in a non-medullated axon. *J. Physiol.*, **107**: 165.

52. HODGKIN, A. L. and HUXLEY, A. F. 1952. A quantitative description of membrane current and its application to conduction and excitation in nerve. *J. Physiol.*, **117**: 500.

53. HODGKIN, A. L., HUXLEY, A. F. and KATZ, B. 1952. Measurement of current-voltage relations in the membrane of the giant axon of *Loligo*. *J. Physiol.*, **116**: 424.

54. HOLMGREN, F. 1865–6. Method att objectivera effecten av ljusentryck på retina. *Uppsala lahref, forh.*, **1**: 177.

55. JACOBSON, S. L. 1965. Receptor response in Venus's fly-trap. *J. gen. Physiol.*, **49**: 117.

56. JIELOF, R., SPOOR, A. and DE VRIES, H. 1952. The microphonic activity of the lateral line. *J. Physiol.*, **116**: 137.

57. KATZ, B. 1937. Experimental evidence for a non-conducted response of nerve to subthreshold stimulation. *Proc. R. Soc.*, ser. B, **124**: 244.

58. —— 1950a. Action potentials from a sensory nerve ending. *J. Physiol.*, **III**: 248.

59. —— 1950b. Depolarization of sensory terminals and the initiation of impulses in the muscle spindle. *J. Physiol.*, **III**: 261.

60. KENNEDY, D. 1958. Responses from the crayfish caudal photoreceptor. *Am. J. Ophthal.*, **46**: II, 19.

61. —— 1960. Neural photoreception in a lamellibranch mollusc. *J. gen. Physiol.*, **44**: 277.

62. —— 1963. Physiology of photoreceptor neurons in the abdominal nerve cord of the crayfish. *J. gen. Physiol.*, **46**: 551.

63. KENNEDY, D. and PRESTON, J. B. 1960. Activity patterns of interneurons in the caudal ganglion of the crayfish. *J. gen. Physiol.*, **43**: 655.

64. KERKUT, G. A. and GARDNER, D. R. 1967. The role of calcium ions in the action potentials of *Helix aspersa* neurones. *Comp. Biochem. Physiol.*, **20**: 147.

65. KRNJEVIC, K. and VAN GELDER, N. M. 1961. Tension changes in crayfish stretch receptors. *J. Physiol.*, **159**: 310.

66. KUFFLER, S. W. 1954. Mechanisms of activation and motor control of stretch receptors in lobster and crayfish. *J. Neurophysiol.*, **17**: 558.

67. LIPPOLD, O. C. J., NICHOLLS, J. G. and REDFEARN, J. W. T. 1960. Electrical and mechanical factors in the adaptation of mammalian muscle spindle. *J. Physiol.*, **153**: 209.

68. LISSMAN, H. W. 1958. On the function and evolution of electric organs in fish. *J. exp. Biol.*, **35**: 156.

69. LISSMAN, H. W. and MACHIN, K. E. 1958. The mechanism of object location in *Gymnarchus niloticus* and similar fish. *J. exp. Biol.*, **35**: 451.

70. LOEWENSTEIN, W. R. 1958. Generator processes of repetitive activity in a Pacinian corpuscle. *J. gen. Physiol.*, **41**: 825.

71. LOEWENSTEIN, W. R. and RATHKAMP, R. 1958. The sites for mechano-electric conversion in a Pacinian corpuscle. *J. gen. Physiol.*, **41**: 1245.

72. LOEWENSTEIN, W. R. and MENDELSON, M. 1965. Components of receptor adaptation in a Pacinian corpuscle. *J. Physiol.*, **177**: 377.

73. LOEWENSTEIN, W. R., TERZUOLO, C. A. and WASHIZU, Y. 1963. Separation of transducer and impulse-generating processes in sensory receptors. *Science*, **142**: 1180.

74. MacNICHOL, E. F., JR. 1958. Subthreshold excitatory processes in the eye of *Limulus*. *Expl. Cell. Res.*, Suppl. **5**: 411.

75. MARKS, W. B. 1965. Visual pigments of single goldfish cones. *J. Physiol.*, **178**: 14.

76. MATTHEWS, B. H. C. 1931. The response of a single end organ. *J. Physiol.*, **71**: 64.

77. MELLON, DeF. 1963. Electrical responses from dually innervated tactile receptors on the thorax of the crayfish. *J. exp. Biol.*, **40**: 137.

78. —— 1967. Analysis of compound action potentials in the central nervous system of the surf clam. *J. gen. Physiol.*, **50**: 759.

79. MELLON, DeF. and KENNEDY, D. 1964. Impulse origin and propagation in a bipolar sensory neuron. *J. gen. Physiol.*, **47**: 487.

80. MENDELSON, M. 1963. Some factors in the activation of crab movement receptors. *J. exp. Biol.*, **40**: 157.

81. —— 1966. The site of impulse initiation in bipolar receptor neurons of *Callinectes sapidus* L. *J. exp. Biol.*, **45**: 311.

82. MENDELSON, M. and LOEWENSTEIN, W. R. 1964. Mechanisms of receptor adaptation. *Science*, **144**: 554.

83. MORITA, H. and YAMASHITA, S. 1959. Generator potential of insect chemoreceptor. *Science*, **130**: 922.

84. NAKA, K. and EGUCHI, E. 1962. Spike potentials recorded from the insect photoreceptor. *J. gen. Physiol.*, **45**: 663.

85. NAKAJIMA, S. 1964. Adaptation in stretch receptor neurons of crayfish. *Science*, **146**: 1168.

86. OTTOSON, D. 1964. The effect of sodium deficiency on the response of the isolated muscle spindle. *J. Physiol.*, **171**: 109.

87. QUILLIAM, T. A. and SATO, M. 1955. The distribution of myelin on nerve fibers from Pacinian corpuscles. *J. Physiol.*, **129**: 167.

88. ROEDER, K. D. and TREAT, A. E. 1961. The detection and evasion of bats by moths. *Am. Scient.*, **49**: 135.

89. RUSHTON, W. A. H. 1956. The difference spectrum and the photo-sensitivity of rhodopsin in the living eye. *J. Physiol.*, **134**: 11.

90. —— 1959. A theoretical treatment of Fuortes' observations upon eccentric cell activity in *Limulus*. *J. Physiol.*, **148**: 29.

91. —— 1961a. Peripheral coding in sensory systems. In: *Sensory Communication* (Ed. W. A. Rosenblith). M.I.T. Press, Cambridge, Mass.

92. —— 1961b. Dark-adaptation and the regeneration of rhodospin. *J. Physiol.*, **156**: 166.

93. —— 1961c. Rhodopsin measurement and dark-adaptation in a subject deficient in cone vision. *J. Physiol.*, **156**: 193.

94. SHERRINGTON, C. S. 1906. *The Integrative Action of the Nervous System.* Cambridge University Press.

95. TAUC, L. 1962. Site of origin and propagation of spike in the giant neuron of *Aplysia*. *J. gen. Physiol.*, **45**: 1077.

96. TERZUOLO, C. A. and WASHIZU, Y. 1962. Relation between stimulus strength, generator potential, and impulse frequency in stretch receptors of Crustacea. *J. Neurophysiol.*, **25**: 56.

97. WALD, G. 1959. The photoreceptor process in vision. In: *Handbook of Physiology. I. Neurophysiology.* American Physiological Society, Washington, D.C.

98. WASHIZU, Y. 1964. Electrical activity of single retinula cells in the compound eye of the blowfly, *Calliphora erythrocephala* Meig. *Comp. Biochem. Physiol.*, **12**: 369.

99. WATANABE, A. and TAKEDA, K. 1963. The change of discharge frequency by a–c stimulus in a weak electric fish. *J. exp. Biol.*, **40**: 57.

100. WATERMAN, T. H. and WIERSMA, C. A. G.  1954.  The functional relation between retinula cells and optic nerve in *Limulus*. *J. exp. Zool.*, **126**: 59.

101. WENDLER, L. and BURKHARDT, D.  1961.  Zeitlich abklingende Vorgänge in der Wirkungskette zwischen Reiz und Erregung (Vorsuche an abdominalen Streckerezeptoren dekapoder Krebse). *Z. Naturf.*, **16b**: 464.

102. WIERSMA, C. A. G., FURSHPAN, E. and FLOREY, E.  1953.  Physiological and pharmacological observations on muscle receptor organs of the crayfish, *Cambarus clarkii*, Girard. *J. exp. Biol.*, **30**: 136.

103. WOLBARSHT, M. L.  1960.  Electrical characteristics of insect mechanoreceptors. *J. gen. Physiol.*, **44**: 105.

104. —— 1965.  Receptor sites in insect chemoreceptors.  In: 'Sensory Receptors.'  *Cold Spring Harb. Symp. quant. Biol.*, **30**: 281

105. WOLBARSHT, M. L. and HANSON, F. E.  1965.  Electrical activity in the chemoreceptors of the blowfly.  III.  Dendritic action potentials. *J. gen. Physiol.*, **48**: 673.

106. WOODBURY, J. W. and PATTON, H. D.  1965.  Action potential; cable and excitable properties of the cell membrane.  In: *Medical Physiology and Biophysics* (Eds. Ruch, T. C. and Patton, F.  19th edn.). W. B. Saunders Co., Philadelphia.

107. WULFF, V. J.  1950.  Duality in the electrical response of the lateral eye of *Limulus polyphemus*. *Biol. Bull.*, **98**: 258.

# Index

This concise summary is the most up-to-date work available on peripheral sensory mechanisms—the physico-chemical, and especially the electrical, events that occur at sensory cells and neurons when exposed to environmental sources of energy.

It begins by introducing the principles of sensory coding, including an electrical description of the nerve impulse; and it suggests reasons for the evolutionary survival of such means of sensory communication. The electrical events which trigger nerve action are examined; and the discovery of 'slow potential phenomena' is shown to have changed the concepts of the response capabilities of nerve cells.

The control of overall membrane polarization in sensory neurons over impulse frequency is examined, and this leads to discussion of membrane time constant, accommodation and refractoriness. Detailed examination is made of structural changes in the sensory membrane that lead to nerve action potential—changes in membrane resistance and the ionic batteries which first generate slow potentials.

The locus of impulse initiation depends on geometrical, spatial and excitability factors. Various preparations for investigating these factors are examined, and difficulties in the way of assessing the function of a particular cell region from purely morphological considerations are pointed out.

The book ends with a discussion of possible methods of investigating the absorption of stimulus energy and the utilization of that energy to produce structural changes in the membrane of the sense cell.

The author is Assistant Professor of Biology at the University of Virginia, Charlottesville.

Net Price **25s**

# UNIVERSITY REVIEWS IN BIOLOGY

# Oliver & Boyd